HEIDELBERG SCIENCE LIBRARY | Volume 16

Introduction to the Physics and Psychophysics of Music

Juan G. Roederer

The English Universities Press Ltd. London

Springer-Verlag New York Heidelberg Berlin

1973

Juan G. Roederer
Professor of Physics
University of Denver
Denver, Colorado, 80210

Cover design by J. G. Roederer. Composed using statistical distribution histograms of time intervals between neural impulses detected by microelectrodes implanted in auditory nerve fibers of cats and squirrel-monkeys (Section 2.8); and oscillograms of second order beats of a mistuned octave (Section 2.6). The author is indebted to Dr. J. E. Rose, University of Wisconsin, for his permission to use a collection of histograms for this purpose (see reference Rose *et al.* 1969, in Chapter 2.)

Dedicated to
the memory
of my dear father

FOREWORD

This book deals with the physical systems and psychophysical processes that intervene in what we broadly call "music." We shall analyze what objective, physical properties of sound patterns are associated with what subjective, psychological sensations of music. We shall describe how these sound patterns are actually produced in musical instruments, how they propagate through the environment, and how they are detected by the ear and interpreted in the brain. We shall do all this by using the physicist's language and his method of thought and analysis—without, however, using complicated mathematics (this, of course, will necessarily impose serious limitations on our presentation). While no previous knowledge of physics is required, it is assumed, however, that the reader is familiar with music, in particular with musical notation, musical scales and intervals, that he has at least some basic ideas about musical instruments, and that he has experienced typical musical "sensations."

Until about 25 years ago, little attention had been paid to the role of the brain, i.e., the central nervous system, in the actual perception, identification, and evaluation of musical sounds. The highly "mechanicistic" approach of 19th-century researchers, notably the great von Helmholz (1863) persisted well into the first half of this century. In this approach the perception of musical tones was regarded mainly as a result of the conversion of certain well-defined sound wave properties (frequency, intensity, and spectrum) into more or less well-defined groups of neural signals (coding information on pitch, loudness, and timbre, respectively) at the level of the inner ear and the peripheral auditory nervous system. Today we know that the central nervous system does play a far more active role in the processing of individual tones, a role so essential that without it the conscious perception of music (and, as a matter of fact, of any other acoustical messages such as language and organized noise) would be impossible. This is why in this book we shall refer a great deal to the discipline of psychophysics, which in a broad sense tries to establish in a quantitative form the causal relationship between the "physical" input from our senses and the psychological sensations and physiological reactions evoked in our mind and body, respectively. Actually, we shall try to weave a rather close mesh between physics and psychophysics—or, more precisely, psychoacoustics. After all, they appear naturally interwoven in music itself: not only pitch, loudness and timbre are a product of physical and psychoacoustical processes, but so are the sensations related to consonance and dissonance, tonic dominance, trills and ornamentation, vibrato, phrasing, beats, tone attack, duration and decay, rhythm, and so on.

Many books on physics of music or musical acoustics are readily available. An up-to-date text is the treatise of John Backus (1969). No book on psychoacoustics is available at the elementary level, though. Several review articles on pertinent topics can be found in Tobias (1970) and in Plomp and Smoorenburg (1970). A comprehensive discussion is given in Flanagan's book on speech (1972). And, of course, there is the classical treatise of von Békésy (1960). A comprehensive up-to-date analysis of general brain processes can be found in Pribram (1971); musical psychology is discussed in classical terms in Lundin (1967). A periodical publishing original research articles on physics of music and psychoacoustics is the *Journal of the Acoustical Society of America*. The purpose of this book is not to duplicate but to synthesize existing literature. The blending of physics and psychoacoustics has been the main guideline followed by the author.

One of the most painful parts of writing a book is deciding what topics should be left out, or grossly neglected, in view of the stringent limitations of space. No matter what the author does, there will always be someone bitterly complaining about this or that omission. Let us list here some of the subjects that have been neglected or omitted—without venturing to attempt a justification. In the discussion of the generation of musical tones mainly basic mechanisms are analyzed, to the detriment of the presentation of concrete musical situations. The human voice has been all but left out and so have discussions of inharmonic tones (percussion instruments) and electronic tone generation; computer-generated music is not even mentioned. On the psychoacoustical side, only the perception of single or multiple *sinusoidal* tones is analyzed, with no word on noise-band or pulse stimuli experiments. Cochlear hydrodynamics and electrophysiology, as well as a description of the neuroanatomy of the auditory tract have had to be omitted, too. And there is practically nothing on rhythm, almost nothing on stereo perception and very little on historical development. Finally, in literature references, priority was given to the quotation of reviews in sources of more widespread availability to the general public; detailed references of original articles can be found in most of the quoted reviews.

This book is an offspring of a syllabus published by the University of Denver for the students in the Physics of Music course, which was introduced at the university in the fall of 1970. In addition to regular classwork, these students are required to perform a series of acoustical and psychoacoustical experiments in a modest laboratory. Conducting such experiments, some of which will be described, is essential for a clear comprehension of the principal physical and psychoacoustical concepts involved. Unfortunately for the general reader, they often require electronic equipment that is not readily available. We ask that the readers trust our description of the experiments and believe that they really do turn out the way we say they do. Whenever possible, we shall indicate how a given experiment can be performed with the aid of ordinary musical equipment.

The author is grateful to Prof. A. H. Benade of Case Western Reserve University (Cleveland), and to Prof. R. T. Schumacher of Carnegie-Mellon University (Pittsburgh) for helpful comments and criticism. Sections 4.5 and 6 of this book are based on recent, still mostly unpublished, work done by Prof. Benade and coworkers. The author also acknowledges with gratitude the efficient secretarial work of Norma Lanier, the expert technical drawing of James Haworth and photographic work of David Clint, and the careful revision of the manuscript by the author's wife, Beatriz.

References

Backus, J. 1969. *The Acoustical Foundations of Music*. W. W. Norton and Company, Inc., New York.

Flanagan, J. L. 1972. *Speech Analysis, Synthesis and Perception*. 2nd ed. Springer-Verlag, New York.

Lundin, R. W. 1967. *An Objective Psychology of Music*. 2nd ed. The Ronald Press Company, New York.

Plomp, R., and G. F. Smoorenburg, editors. 1970. *Frequency Analysis and Periodicity Detection in Hearing*. A. W. Suithoff, Leiden.

Pribram, K. H. 1971. *Languages of the Brain*. Prentice-Hall, Inc., Englewood Cliffs, N.J.

Tobias, J. V., editor. 1970. *Foundations of Modern Auditory Theory*. Academic Press, New York.

von Békésy, G. 1960. *Experiments in Hearing*. McGraw Hill Book Co., New York.

von Helmoltz, H. 1863. *On the Sensations of Tone as a Physiological Basis for the Theory of Music*. English translation, 1954. Dover Publ., New York.

CONTENTS

MUSIC, PHYSICS, AND PSYCHOPHYSICS: AN INTERDISCIPLINARY APPROACH

1.1 The Intervening Physical Systems

Imagine yourself in a concert hall listening to a soloist performing. Let us identify the systems that are relevant to the "music" you hear. First, obviously, we have the player and the *instrument* that "makes" the music. Second, we have the *air* in the hall that transmits the sound into all directions. Third, there is you, the *listener*. In other words, we have the chain of systems: instrument → air → listener. What links them while music is being played? A certain type and form of vibrations called *sound* which propagate from one point to another in the form of *waves* and to which our ear is sensitive. (There are many other types and forms of vibrations that we cannot detect at all, or that we may detect, but with other senses such as touch or vision.)

The physicist uses more general terms to describe the three systems listed above. He calls them: *source* → *medium* → *receptor*. This chain of systems is common to the study of many other physical processes: light, radioactivity, electricity, gravity, cosmic rays, etc. The source *emits*, the medium *transmits*, the receptor *detects*, registers, or, in general, is affected in some specific way. What is emitted, transmitted, and detected is energy—in one of its multiple forms, depending on the particular case envisaged. In the case of sound waves, it is *elastic* energy, because it involves oscillations of pressure, that is, rapidly alternating compressions and expansions of air.

Let us have a second, closer, look at the systems involved. At the source, i.e., the musical instrument, we identify several distinct components: (1) The *primary excitation mechanism* that must be activated by the player,[1] such as the bowing or the plucking action on a violin

---

[1] To make the description complete we might add the *player* and his multiple

string, the oscillating reed in a clarinet, the player's lips in a brass instrument, or the airstream blown against a wedge in the flute. This excitation mechanism acts as the primary energy source. (2) The fundamental *vibrating element* that, when excited by the primary mechanism, is capable of sustaining certain well-defined vibration modes of prefixed frequencies, such as the strings of a violin or the air column in the bore of a wind instrument or organ pipe. This vibrating element actually determines the musical pitch of the tone and, as a fortunate bonus, provides the upper harmonics needed to impart a certain characteristic quality to the tone. In addition, it serves as a vibrational energy storage. In wind instruments it partly controls the primary excitation mechanism through feedback coupling (strong in woodwinds, weak in brasses). (3) Many instruments have an additional *resonator* (sound board of a piano, body of a string instrument) whose function is to convert more efficiently the oscillations of the primary vibrating element (string) into sound vibrations of the surrounding air.

In the medium, too, we must make a distinction: we have the *medium proper* that transmits the sound and the *boundaries,* i.e., the walls, the ceiling, the floor, the people in the audience, etc., which strongly affect the sound propagation by *reflection* and *absorption* of the sound waves and whose configuration determines the quality of room acoustics (reverberation).

Finally, in the listener we single out the following principal components: (1) The *eardrum,* which picks up the pressure oscillations of the sound wave reaching the ear and converts them into mechanical vibrations that are transmitted via a link of three tiny bones to: (2) The *inner ear,* or cochlea, in which the vibrations are sorted out according to frequency ranges, picked up by receptor cells, and converted into nerve impulses. (3) The *auditory nervous system,* which transmits the neural signals to the brain where the information is processed, displayed as an image of auditory features on a certain area of the cortex (the brain surface and underlying tissue), identified, stored in the memory, and eventually transferred to other centers of the brain. These latter stages lead to the conscious perception of musical sounds. Some neural processing of acoustical information is done right at the outset in the peripheral nervous system (adaptation, contrast intensification, and, very likely, detection of transients).

Notice that we may replace the listener by a *recording device* such as a magnetic tape recorder, a phonograph recorder, or a photoelectric record on film, and still recognize at least three of the subsystems:

"components": the motor cortex of his brain that issues the commands to his muscles, the parts of his body with which he activates the musical instrument or his vocal tract, the feedback from ears and muscles that aids him in controlling his performance, etc. But, unfortunately, limitation of space compels us to leave the player completely out of the picture.

the mechanical detection and subsequent conversion into electrical signals in the microphone, a limited amount of deliberate or accidental processing in the electronic circuitry, and the memory storage on tape, disc, or film, respectively. The first system, i.e., the instrument, of course also may be replaced by an electronic *playing device.*

We may summarize this discussion in Table 1.1.

Table 1.1

	System	*Function*
Source	Excitation mechanism	energy supply
	Vibrating element	determination of fundamental tone characteristics
	Resonator	conversion into air pressure oscillations (sound waves), final determination of tone characteristics
Medium	Medium proper	sound propagation
	Boundaries	reflection, absorption, reverberation
Receptor	Eardrum	conversion into mechanical oscillations
	Inner ear	primary frequency sorting, conversion into nerve impulses
	Nervous system	processing, display, identification, storage and transfer to other brain centers

The main aim of this book is to analyze comprehensively what happens at each stage shown in Table 1.1 and during each transition from one stage to the next, when music is being played.

1.2 Characteristic Attributes of Musical Sounds

Subjects from all cultures agree that there are three primary sensations associated with a given single musical sound: *pitch, loudness,* and *quality.*[2] We shall not attempt to define these subjective attributes or psychological magnitudes, or get involved at this stage in the discussion of whether they are measurable; we shall just note that pitch is frequently described as the sensation of "altitude" or "height," and loudness that of "strength" or "intensity" of a tone. Quality, or timbre, is what enables us to distinguish among sounds from different kinds of instruments even if their pitch and loudness are the same. The unambiguous association of these three qualities to a given sound is what differentiates a musical "tone" from "noise": although we can definitely assign loudness

---

[2] The sometimes quoted sensations of *volume* and *density* (or brightness) are composite concepts that can be "resolved" into a combination of pitch and loudness effects (lowering of pitch with simultaneous increase of loudness leads to a sensation of increased volume; rising pitch with simultaneous increase of loudness leads to increased density or brightness).

3

to a given noise, it is far more difficult to identify a unique pitch or quality.

The assignment of pitch, loudness, and quality to a musical sound is the result of processing operations in the ear and in the brain. It is subjective and inaccessible to direct physical measurement (see Section 1.4). However, each one of these primary sensations can be associated in principle to a well-defined physical quantity of the original stimulus, i.e., the sound wave, that can be measured and expressed numerically by physical methods. Indeed, the sensation of pitch is primarily associated to the *fundamental frequency* (repetition rate of the vibration pattern, described by the number of oscillations per second), loudness to *intensity* (energy flow or pressure oscillation amplitude of the sound wave reaching the ear), and quality to the *spectrum,* or proportion with which other, higher, frequencies called "upper harmonics" appear mixed with each other and accompany the fundamental frequency.

This, however, is a far too simplistic picture. First, the pitch sensation caused by a pure tone of fixed frequency does change slightly if we change the intensity; conversely, the loudness of a tone of constant intensity will appear to vary if we change the frequency. Second, the sensation of loudness of a superposition of several tones of different pitch each is not any more related in a simple way to the total sound energy flow; for a succession of tones of very short duration on the other hand, it depends on how long each tone actually lasts. Third, refined timbre perception as required for musical instrument recognition is a process that utilizes much more information than just the spectrum of a tone: the transient attack and decay characteristics are equally important, as one may easily verify by trying to recognize musical instruments while listening to a magnetic tape played backward. Moreover, the tones of a given instrument may have spectral characteristics that change appreciably throughout the compass of the instrument, and the spectral composition of a given tone may change considerably from point to point in a music hall; yet they are recognized without hesitation as pertaining to the same instrument. Conversely, a highly trained musician may have greatest difficulty in matching the exact pitch of a single electronically generated tone deprived of upper harmonics, fed to his ears through headphones, because his central nervous system is lacking some key additional information that normally comes with the "real" sounds to which he is exposed.

Another relevant physical characteristic of a tone is the spatial direction from which the corresponding sound wave is arriving. What really matters here is the minute time difference between the acoustical signals detected at each ear, which depends on the direction of incidence. This time difference is measured and coded by the nervous system to yield the sensation of *tone directionality* (stereophony or binaural fusion).

When two or more tones are sounded simultaneously, our brain is capable of singling them out individually, within certain limitations. New, less well-defined but nevertheless musically essential subjective sensations appear in connection with two or more superposed tones, collectively leading to the concept of *harmony*. Among them are the "static" sensations of *consonance and dissonance* describing the either "pleasing" or "irritating" character of certain superpositions of tones, the "dynamic" sensation of the *urge to resolve* a given dissonant interval or chord, the peculiar effect of *beats,* and the different character of *major* and *minor* chords. Whereas the correlation of pitch, loudness, and, to some extent, quality with certain physical characteristics of single tones is "universal"—i.e., independent of the cultural conditioning of a given individual—this is no longer the case with the above-mentioned subjective attributes of tone superpositions.

1.3 The Time Element in Music

A steady sound, with constant frequency, intensity, and spectrum is annoying. Moreover, after a while our conscient present wouldn't register it any more. Only when that sound is turned off do we suddenly realize again that it had been there. Music is made up of tones whose physical characteristics change with time in a certain fashion. It is only this time dependence that makes a sound "musical" in the true sense. In general, we shall henceforth call a time sequence of individual tones, or superposition of tones, a *musical message*. Such a musical message may or may not be "meaningful" (sometimes called a tonal "Gestalt"), depending on whether we assign a certain value to it as the result of a series of brain operations of analysis, comparison with previously stored messages, storage in the memory, and associations. A *melody* is the most relevant example of a musical message. Some attributes of "meaningful" musical messages are key elements in music: *tonality* (domination of a single tone in the sequence), the *sense of return* to the tonic, *modulation*, and *rhythm*. A fundamental characteristic of a melody is that the succession of tones proceeds in discrete, finite steps of pitch in practically all musical cultures. Out of the infinite number of available frequencies, our auditory system prefers to single out discrete values corresponding to the notes of a *musical scale,* even though we are able to detect frequency changes that are much smaller than the natural step of any musical scale. The neural mechanism that analyzes a musical message pays attention only to the *transitions* of pitch; "absolute" pitch processing is lost at an early age in most individuals.

Let us examine the time element in music more closely. There are three distinct time scales on which time variations of psychoacoustical relevance occur. First, we have the "microscopic" time scale, in which the actual vibrations of a sound wave occur, covering a range from about 0.00007 to 0.05 seconds. Then there is an "intermediate" range centered at about one-tenth of a second, in which some transient changes such as tone attack and decay occur, representing the time variations of the microscopic features. Finally, we have the "macroscopic" time scale, ranging from about 0.1 second upward, corresponding to common musical tone durations, successions, and rhythm. It is important to note that each typical time scale has a particular "processing center" with a specific function, in the auditory system. (1) The microscopic vibrations are detected and coded in the *inner ear* and mainly lead to the primary tone sensations (pitch, loudness, and quality). (2) The intermediate or transient variations seem to affect mainly processing mechanisms in the *neural pathway* from the ear to the auditory area in the brain and provide additional cues for quality perception, tone identification, and discrimination. (3) The macroscopic time changes are processed at the highest neural level—the *cerebral cortex,* the folded structure and underlying tissue forming the major part of the brain; they determine the actual musical message and its attributes.

The higher we move up through these processing stages in the auditory pathway, the more difficult it becomes to define and identify the psychological attributes to which this processing leads and the more everything appears to be influenced by learning and cultural conditioning, as well as by the momentaneous behavioral state of the individual. This gradually increasing complexity was probably dictated by the ever-increasing demands on the auditory system, first as a distance receptor and later as a communications device, in the course of biological evolution.

The "intermediate" and "macroscopic" time changes and their psychological effects have been very much neglected in experimental psychoacoustical research. For more than 100 years musicologists have bitterly complained that physics of music and psychoacoustics have been restricted mainly to the study of steady, constant tones or tone complexes, whereas the essence of music is a time sequence thereof. Their complaints are well founded, but the reasons for such a restriction are well founded, too. As explained above, the processing of tone sequences occurs at the highest level of the central nervous system—involving an as yet little explored chain of mechanisms. In this book, whenever possible, we shall try to remedy this situation and go as far as we can to dispel some of this well-placed criticism.

1.4 Physics and Psychophysics

We may describe the principal objective of physics in the following way: to provide methods by means of which one can predict quantitatively the evolution of a given physical system, based on the conditions in which the system is found initially. For instance, given an automobile of a certain mass and specifying the braking forces, physics allows us to predict how long it will take to bring the car to a halt and where it will come to a stop, provided we specify the position and the speed at the initial instant of time. Given the mass, the length, and the tension of a violin string, physics predicts the possible frequencies with which the string would vibrate if plucked or bowed in a certain manner. Given the shape and dimensions of an organ pipe and the composition and the temperature of the gas inside (air), physics predicts the fundamental frequency of the sound emitted when it is blown.

In practice, "to predict" means to provide a mathematical apparatus, a series of formulas or "recipes" which, based on certain *physical laws* that govern the system under analysis, establish mathematical relationships between the values of the physical magnitudes that characterize the system at any given instant of time (position and speed in the case of the car; frequency and amplitude of oscillation in the other two examples.) These relations are then used to find out how the values change as time progresses.

In order to establish the physical laws that govern a given system, we must first observe the system and make quantitative measurements of the physical magnitudes to find out their causal interrelationships experimentally. A physical law expresses a certain relationship that is common to many different physical systems and independent of particular circumstances. For instance, the law governing gravitation is valid here on earth, on the moon, in the solar system, and elsewhere in the universe. Newton's law of motion applies to all bodies, irrespective of their chemical composition, color, temperature, speed, or position.

Most of the actual systems studied in physics—even the "simple" and "familiar" examples given above—are so complex, that accurate and detailed predictions are impossible. Thus, we must make approximations and devise simplified *models* that represent a given system only by its main features. Many times it is necessary to break up the system under study into a series of more elementary subsystems, physically interacting with each other, each one governed by a well-defined set of physical laws.

The physics of daily life's world, or *classical physics*, assumes that both measurements and predictions should always be "exact" and "unique," the only limitations and errors being due to the imperfection of our measuring or observing devices. In the atomic and subatomic domain, however, this deterministic view does not apply any more. Nature is such that measurements and predictions of an atomic system can *never* be expected to be exact or unique in the ordinary sense, no matter how much we try to improve our techniques: measurements will always be of limited accuracy and only *probabilities*, that is likelihood, can be predicted for the values of physical magnitudes in the atomic domain. In other words, it is impossible to predict, say, *when* a given radioactive nucleus will decay, or exactly *where* a given electron will be found at a given time during its journey from the cathode to the TV screen—only probabilities can be specified. An entirely new physics had to be constructed in the early 1920's, fit to describe atomic and subatomic systems—the so-called *quantum physics.*

The reader may wonder at this stage why we are talking about quantum physics, when it seems to be totally irrelevant to the study of sound and music. However, *psychophysics* operates in a fashion that in some aspects is surprisingly similar to quantum physics. First of all, as physics in general, psychophysics tries to make predictions on the evolution of a specific system subjected to given initial conditions. The system under consideration is the *brain and associated peripheral nervous and endocrine systems,* the conditions are determined by the physical *sensorial input stimuli,* and the evolution is manifested by the individual physiological reactions or by the whole complex *behavior* of the body commanded by that brain. In man, who is able to report verbally the results of an introspective observation of his own state of mind, the evolution of the psychophysical system is usually described by the *psychological sensations* and feelings evoked by the sensorial stimuli (this is sometimes called sensory psychophysics in distinction to the above motor psychophysics). Like physics, psychophysics requires that the causal relationship between physical stimulus input and behavioral or psychological output be established through experimentation and measurement. Like physics, psychophysics must make simplifying assumptions and construct *models*—mainly for nervous and neuropsychological systems operations—in order to be able to venture into the business of prediction-making.

Unlike classical physics, but strikingly similar to quantum physics, psychophysical predictions can never be expected to be exact or unique—only probability values can be established. Unlike classical physics, but strikingly similar to quantum physics, most measurements in psychophysics will substantially perturb the system under observation, and nothing can be done to eliminate said perturbation completely. As a consequence, the result of a measurement does not reflect the state of "the system per se," but, rather, the more complex state of "the system under observation." Also as a result, psychophysics requires experimentation with many different equivalent (but never identical) systems (subjects), and a *statistical interpretation* of the results.[3]

Quite obviously, there are some limits to these analogies. In physics,

---

[3] We must emphasize that these are only *analogies.* Quantum physics *as such* does not play an explicit role in the nervous system, whose operation is based on eminently classical processes (though individual quantum-mechanical interactions may play an explicit role in the mechanism of transmission of neural signals from one cell to another).

the process or "recipe" of the measurement which defines a given physical magnitude, such as the length, weight, or velocity of an object, can be formulated in a rigorous, unambiguous way. As long as we deal with physiological output, such as neural impulse rate, amplitude of evoked goosepimples or increase in heartbeat, measurements can be formulated in a rigorous, unambiguous way, too. But in sensory psychophysics, how do we define and measure the subjective sensations of pitch, loudness, or—to make it even more tricky—the magnitude that represents the urge to bring a given melody to its tonic completion? Or how would we arrange measurements on "internal hearing," i.e., the action of provoking musical tone sensations by volition, without external stimuli? Could this be done by interrogation alone, or must we resort to "direct" measurements via implantation of microelectrodes into brain cells?

It is now believed that a given sensation is related to neural activity, evoked by sensory input signals, and "displayed" on the cortical area to which the stimulated sense organ is wired (primary auditory receiving area, visual cortex, etc.). Whenever the "read-out" mechanism that represents our conscient present, and whose function is to monitor and synthesize the image of environmental features continuously being displayed on the sensory cortex areas, directs its attention to the particular area in question, the encountered activity gives rise to what we report as a "sensation." The general location and the spatial and temporal distribution of this neural activity determine the class and the subjective "intensity" of the associated sensation. Many sensations can indeed be *classified* into more or less well-defined types (called sensorial qualities, if they are caused by the same sense organ)—the fact that people do report to each other on pitch, loudness, tone quality, consonance, etc., without much mutual misunderstanding with regard to the meaning of these concepts, is an example. Furthermore, two sensations belonging to the same type, experienced one following the other, can in general be *ordered* by the experiencing subject as to whether the specific attribute of one is felt to be "greater" (or "higher," "stronger," "brighter," "more pronounced," etc.), "equal," or "less" than the other. For instance, when presented with two tones in a succession, the subject can judge whether the second tone was of higher, equal, or lower pitch than the first one. Another example of ordering is the following: presented with the choice of three complex tones of the same pitch and loudness, he may order them in pairs by judging which two tones have the most similar timbre and which the most dissimilar one.

The ability, possessed by all individuals, to classify and order subjective sensations gives subjective sensations a status quite equivalent to that of a physical magnitude and justifies the introduction of the term *psychophysical magnitude*. What we must *not* pretend a priori is to expect that individuals can judge whether a sensation of, say, loudness is "twice" or "half," or any other numerical factor, that of a reference "unit" sensation. Our brain simply is not equipped a priori with the necessary operational device for a quantitative intercomparison or measurement. It is like asking for an accuracy in atomic measurements that exceeds the limit imposed by mother nature, i.e., by quantum physics. There are situations, however, in which it is possible to *learn* to make quantitative estimates of psychophysical magnitudes on a statistical basis, and, in some instances, the brain may become very good at it, indeed. The visual sense is an example. After sufficient experience, the estimation of the size of objects can become highly accurate, provided enough information about the given object is available; judgments such as "twice as long" or "half as tall," are made without hesitation. It is quite clear from this example that a "unit" and the corresponding psychophysical process of comparison have been built into the brain only *through experience and learning,* in multiple contacts with the original physical magnitudes. The same can be achieved with other psychophysical sensations such as loudness: it is necessary to acquire through learning the ability of comparison and quantitative judgment. The fact that musicians all over the world use a common loudness notation—maybe without ever having heard of sonometers and decibels—is a self-evident example.

And here we come to the perhaps most crucial differences between physics and psychophysics: (1) repeated measurements of the same kind may *condition the response* of the psychophysical system under observation: the brain has the ability of learning, gradually changing the course of response probability to a given input stimulus, as the number of similar exposures increases. (2) The *free will* of the subject under study and the consequences thereof, mental or physical, may interfere in a highly unpredictable way with the measurements. As a consequence of the first point, a statistical psychophysical study with one single individual exposed to repeated "measurements" will by no means be identical to a statistical study involving one single measurement performed on each one of many different individuals. This difference is due not only to differences among individuals, but also to the conditioning that takes place in the case of repeated exposures. The ultracomplex feedback systems in the nervous system make psychoacoustical measurements particularly tricky to set up and to interpret. The consequences of point (2) may be even more far-reaching, particularly for investigations about the role of the conscious self.

1.5 What is Music?

The previous discussion may have irritated some readers. Music, they will say, is "pure aesthetics," a manifestation of the innate and sublime human comprehension of the beautiful rather than the mere effect of certain sound wave stimuli on a complex network of billions of nerve cells. However, for the psychophysicist *even aesthetic feelings must ultimately be somehow related to neural information-processing.* The so-characteristic blend of regular, ordered patterns alternated with surprise and uncertainty, common to all sensorial input judged as "aesthetic," may ultimately be a manifestation of man's innate desire to exercise his superredundant neural network with nonessential information-processing operations of changing or alternating complexity—just for the fun of it! Music, as a matter of fact, seems to be a quite natural byproduct of the evolution of speech and language. In this evolution, which undoubtedly *was* an essential factor for the development of the human race, a neural network emerged, capable of executing the ultra-complex sound processing, identification, and storage and retrieval operations necessary for phonetic recognition, voice identification, and comprehension of words and sentences. In the course of this evolution astounding redundancies, safeguards, and back-up systems were built in, with the end result that language is only being processed in *one* cerebral hemisphere (for most individuals, the left side), leaving the almost identical auditory neural network of the other hemisphere free "to do what it pleases" with the incoming information.[4] And, very likely, this is how the processing of music comes about.

Since the perception of music is ultimately based on acoustical information-processing, the major or minor degree of complexity of a tone message identification, the degree of success of prediction-making operations that are carried out by the brain to expedite this identification process[5] and the type of associations evoked by comparison with stored information on previous experiences may all together be the ultimate "cause" of the musical sensations evoked by a given musical message. If this is true, it would be quite obvious that both innate neural mechanisms (primary processing operations) *and* cultural conditioning (stored messages and learned processing operations) must determine our behavioral and aesthetic response to music.

---

[4] Tests with brain-damaged patients convincingly show that a person who has lost language comprehension and speech may still be able to hum a melody (and even phonetically reproduce the words—without understanding them), and comprehend music, without impairment.

[5] We should point out that, quite generally, the development of a high-speed prediction-making capability must have been a leading motivation for the evolution of the central nervous system, in order to endow the higher species with predictor-corrector mechanisms that were necessary to enhance their chance of survival in an ecological environment of ever-increasing complexity.

CHAPTER 2

SOUND VIBRATIONS, PURE TONES, AND THE PERCEPTION OF PITCH

We hear a "sound" when the eardrum is set into a characteristic type of periodic motion called *vibration*. This vibration is caused by small pressure oscillations of the air in the auditory canal associated to an incoming sound wave. In this chapter we shall first discuss the fundamentals of vibratory motion in general and then focus on the effects of eardrum vibrations on our sensation of hearing. We shall not worry at this stage about *how* the eardrum is set into motion. To that effect, let us imagine that we put on headphones and listen to tones generated therein. The eardrums will follow very closely the vibrations of the headphone diaphragms. This approach of introducing the subject is somewhat unorthodox. But it will enable us to plunge straight into the study of some of the key concepts associated with sound vibration and sound perception without spending first a long time on sound waves and sound generation. From the practical point of view, this approach has one drawback: the experiments that we shall present and analyze in this chapter necessarily require electronic generation of sound rather than natural production with real musical instruments. Whenever possible, however, we shall indicate how a given experiment could be performed with real instruments.

2.1 Motion and Vibration

Motion means *change of position* of a given body with respect to some reference body. If the moving body is very small with respect to the reference body, or with respect to the dimensions of the spatial domain covered in its motion, so that its shape is practically irrelevant, the problem is reduced to the description of the motion of a *point* in space. This is why such a small body is often called a material point or a particle. On the other hand, if the body is not small, but if from the particular circumstances we know beforehand that all points of the body are confined to move along straight lines parallel to each other ("rectilinear translation"), it, too, will suffice to specify the motion of just *one* given point of the body. This is a "one-dimensional" case of motion, and the position of the given point of the body (and, hence, that of the whole body) is completely specified by just *one* number: the distance to a fixed reference point.

In this book we shall only deal with one-dimensional motions. Let us assume that our material point moves along a vertical line (Fig. 2.1). We shall designate the reference point on that line with the letter

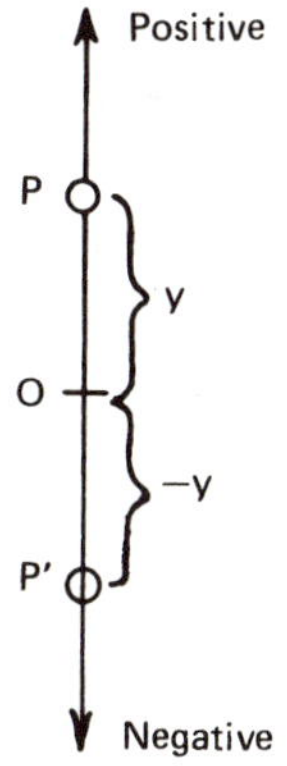

Fig. 2.1

O. Any fixed point can serve as a reference point, although, for convenience, we sometimes may select a particular one (such as the equilibrium position for a given oscillatory motion). We indicate the position of a material point P by the distance y to the reference point O (Fig. 2.1). y is also called the *displacement* of P with respect to O, or the *coordinate* of P. We must use both positive and negative numbers to distinguish between the two sides with respect to O.

In physics, the *metric system* is used to measure distances. The unit of length is the *meter* (1 m = 3.28 feet); several decimal submultiples (e.g., the centimeter = 0.01 m = 0.394 inch, or the millimeter = 0.001 m) and multiples (e.g., the kilometer = 1000 m = 0.625 mile) are also frequently used.

The material point P is in motion with respect to O when its position changes with time. We shall indicate time by the letter t. It is measured with a clock—and it, too, requires that we specify a "reference" instant of time at $t = 0$. Motion can be represented mathematically in two ways: analytically, using so-called functional relationships, and geometrically, using a graphical representation. We shall use only the geometric method. To represent a one-dimensional motion graphically, we introduce two axes perpendicular to each other, one representing the time t, the other the coordinate y (Fig. 2.2). For both we have to indicate clearly the *scale*, i.e., the unit intervals (of time and displacement, respectively). A motion can be represented by plotting for each instant of time t, the distance y at which the particle is momentarily located. Each point of the ensuing curve, such as S_1, (Fig. 2.2), tells us that at $t = t_1$ the particle P is at a distance y_1 from O, i.e., at position P_1. Note very carefully that in this graph the material point does *not* move along the curve of points S. This curve is just a human-made "aid" that helps us to find the position y of the particle at any time t.

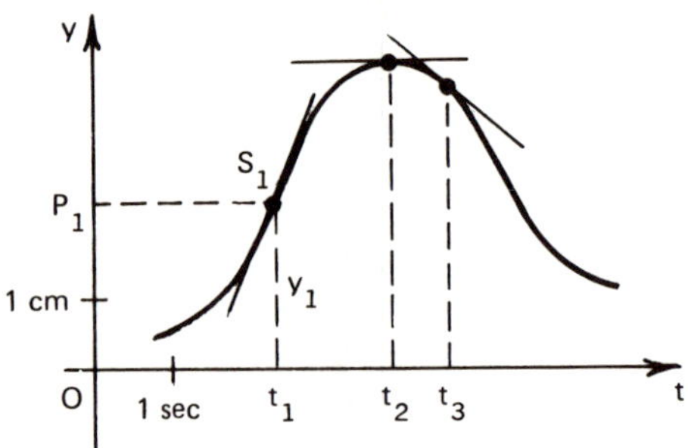

Fig. 2.2

The graph of Fig. 2.2 also gives information on the velocity of the material point, i.e., the rate of change of its position. This is determined by the *slope* of the curve in the graph: at t_1 the particle is moving at a certain rate upward, at t_3 it is moving downward at a slower rate. At t_2 it is momentarily at rest, reversing its direction.

There is a certain class of motions in which the material point follows a pattern that is repeated time and again. This is called *periodic motion*, or *vibration*. It is the type of motion of greatest importance to physics of music. In order to have a truly periodic motion, a body not only has to come back to the same position repeatedly, it has to do so at exactly equal intervals of time and repeat exactly the same type of motion in between. The interval of time after which the pattern of motion is repeated is called the *period* (Fig. 2.3a). We denote it by the Greek letter tau (τ). During one period the motion may be very simple (Fig. 2.3a) or rather complicated (Fig. 2.3b). The elementary pattern of motion that occurs during one period and that is repeated over and over again is called a *cycle*.

There are mechanical and electronic devices that can automatically plot the graph of a periodic motion. In a *chart-recorder*, the pen reproduces in the y direction the periodic motion that is to be described,

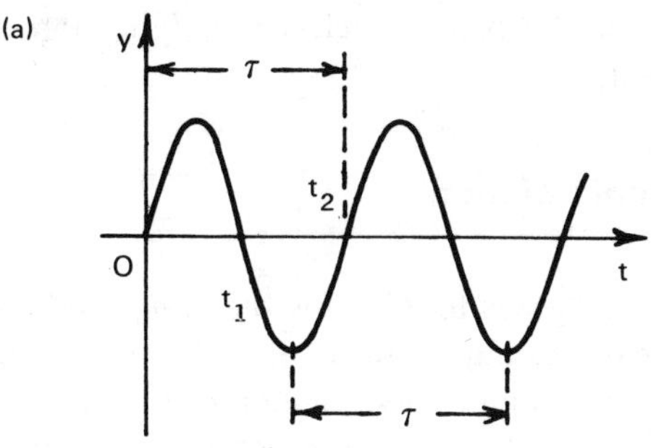

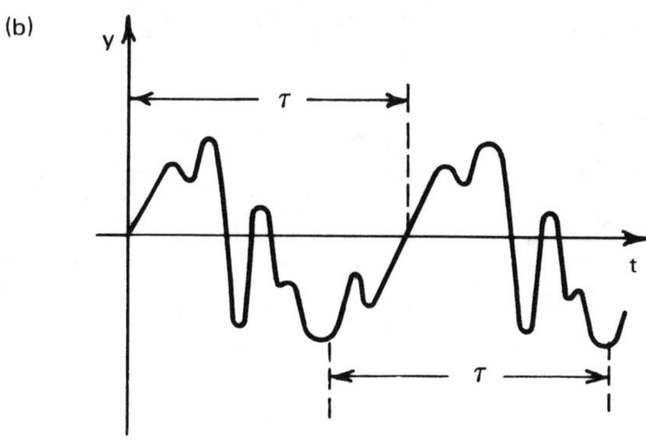

Fig. 2.3

while it is writing on a strip of paper that is moving perpendicularly to the y axis at a constant speed. Since we know this speed, we can assign a *time* scale to the axis along the paper strip. The curve obtained is the graphical representation of the motion. This method is not practical for the registration of acoustical vibrations though. They have such short periods that it would be impossible to displace a pen fast enough to reproduce this type of vibration. An electronic device called *oscilloscope* serves the purpose. In essence, it consists of a very narrow beam of electrons (elementary particles of negative electric charge) that impinge on a TV-type screen giving a clearly visible light spot. This beam can be deflected both in the vertical and in the horizontal directions. The vertical motion is controlled by a signal proportional to the vibration which we want to display (for instance, the vibration of the diaphragm of an earphone). The horizontal motion is a continuous sweep to the right with constant speed, equivalent to the motion of the paper strip in a chart recorder, thus representing a time scale. The luminous point on the screen thus describes the graph of the motion during one sweep. If the image of the luminous point is retained long enough, it appears as a continuous curve on the screen. Since the screen is only of limited size, the horizontal motion is instantaneously reset to the origin whenever the beam reaches the right edge of the screen, and the sweep starts again.

2.2 Simple Harmonic Motion

The question now arises as to which is the *"simplest"* kind of periodic motion. There are many examples in nature: the back and forth oscillation of a pendulum, the up and down motion of a spring, the oscillations of molecules, etc. Their motions have something important in common: they all can be represented as the projection of a uniform circular motion onto one diameter of the circle (Fig. 2.4).[1] When point R turns around

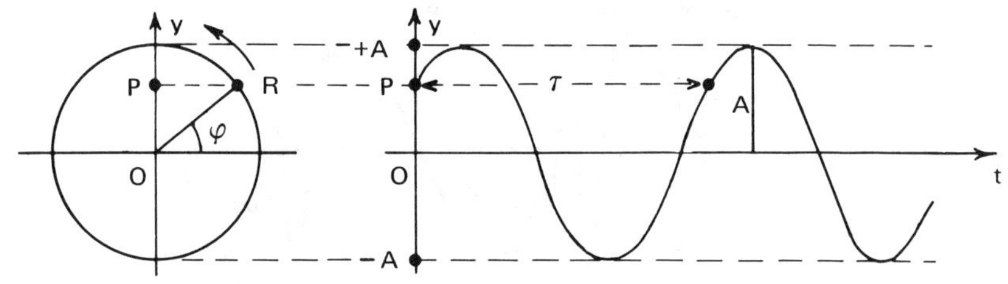

Fig. 2.4

uniformly (with period τ, i.e., once every τ seconds) the projection point P moves up and down along the y axis with what is called a *simple harmonic motion* (see graph at right side of Fig. 2.4). This is also called a *sinusoidal motion* (because y can be represented analytically by a trigonometric function called sine).

Note that a simple harmonic motion represents a vibration that is symmetric with respect to point O, which is called the equilibrium position. The maximum displacement A (either up or down) is called *amplitude*. τ is the *period* of the harmonic motion. There is one more parameter describing simple harmonic motion, that is a little more difficult to understand. Consider Fig. 2.4: at the initial instant $t = 0$, the particle (projection of the rotating point R) is located at position P. We may now envisage a second case of harmonic motion with the *same* period τ and the *same* amplitude A, but in which the particle starts from a *different position Q* (Fig. 2.5). The resulting motion obviously will be different, not in form or type, but in relative "timing." Indeed, as seen in Fig. 2.5, both particles will pass through a given position (e.g., the origin O) at different times (t_1, t_2). Conversely, both particles will in

---

[1] Note carefully that the construction at the left side of Fig. 2.4 is *auxiliary;* the only real motion is the periodic up-and-down motion of the particle P along the y axis.

general be at different positions at one given time (e.g., *P* and *Q* at $t = 0$). If we again imagine the motion of the second particle *Q* as the projection of a uniform circular motion (Fig. 2.5), we realize that both cases pertain to different *angular positions* φ_1, φ_2 of the associated rotating points on the circle. The angle φ is called the *phase* of a simple harmonic motion; the difference $\varphi_1 - \varphi_2$ (Fig. 2.5), which remains constant in this example, is called the *phase difference* between the two harmonic motions.

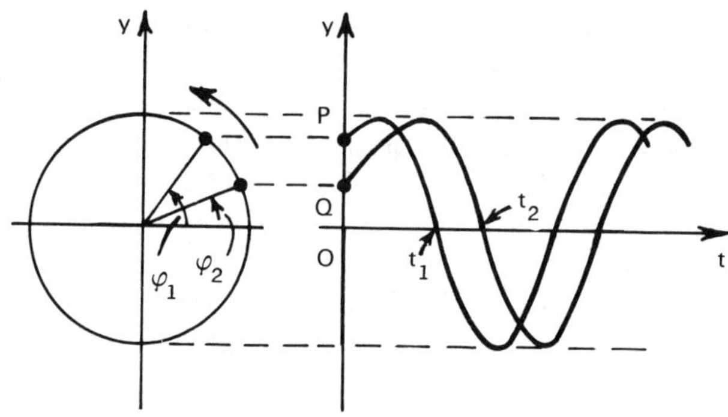

Fig. 2.5

In summary, a given "pure," or harmonic, vibration is specified by the values of three parameters: the *period* τ, the *amplitude* A, and the *phase* φ (Fig. 2.4). They all, but especially the first two, play a key role in the perception of musical sounds.

Simple harmonic motions occur practically everywhere in the universe: vibrations of the constituents of the atoms, of the atoms as a whole in a crystal, of elastic bodies, etc., can all be described in terms of simple harmonic motions. But there is another even more powerful reason for considering simple harmonic motion as the most basic periodic motion of all: it can be shown mathematically that *any kind of periodic motion, however complicated, can be described as a sum of simple harmonic vibrations.* We shall deal with this fundamental property later on in detail (Chapter 4). It is indeed of capital importance to music.

2.3 Acoustical Vibrations and Pure Tone Sensations

When the eardrum is set into periodic motion, its mechanical vibrations are converted in the inner ear into nerve impulses that are signaled to the brain and interpreted as sound, provided the period and the amplitude of the vibrations lie within certain limits. In general, the ear is an extremely sensitive device: vibration amplitudes of the eardrum as small as 10^{-7} cm can be detected, and so can vibrations with periods as short as 7×10^{-5} sec.[2]

We now introduce a quantity that is used more frequently than the period τ, called the *frequency:*

$$f = \frac{1}{\tau} \tag{2.1}$$

Physically, f represents the number of repetitions of the vibration pattern, or cycles, in the unit of time. The reason for preferring f to τ is that the frequency increases when our sensation of "tone-height" or pitch increases. If τ is given in seconds, f is expressed in *cycles per second.* This unit is called Hertz (Hz), in honor of Heinrich Hertz, the famous German physicist. Vibrations in the interval 20 Hz–15,000 Hz are sensed as "sound" by a normal person. Both the lower and particularly the upper limit depend on tone loudness and vary considerably from person to person and with age.

When a sound causes a simple harmonic motion of the eardrum with constant characteristics (frequency, amplitude, phase), we hear what is called a *pure tone.* A pure tone sounds dull, and music is not made up of single pure tones. However, as stated in the introduction to this chapter, for a better understanding of complex sounds, it is advisable to deal first with pure or simple tones only. Pure tones have to be generated with electronic oscillators; there is no musical instrument that produces them (and even for electronically generated pure tones, there is no guarantee that they will be "pure" when they actually reach our ear). In any case, since the flute is the instrument whose sound approximates that of a pure, sinusoidal tone more than any other instrument, especially in the upper register, several (but not all) of the experiments referred to in this chapter can indeed be performed at home using one or, as a matter of fact, two flutes—played by experts, though!

When we listen to a pure tone whose frequency and amplitude can be changed at will, we verify a correspondence between *pitch* and *frequency* and between *loudness* and *amplitude.* One has a fairly good idea on how the ear's primary frequency and amplitude detection mechanism works for pure sounds. In this chapter we only consider pitch. The simple harmonic oscillations of the eardrum are transmitted by a chain of three small bones (called hammer, anvil, and stirrup) to a membrane at the entrance (oval window) to the *cochlear duct,* which represents the inner ear proper (Fig. 2.6). This duct, wound up like a snail's shell (in Fig. 2.6b it is shown "stretched out"), is partitioned longitudinally into two tubes by the *basilar membrane,* about 3.5 cm long, which holds the actual sensor organ (organ of Corti) and cor-

---

[2] In this book we shall use the exponent notation: $10^{+n} = 1\overbrace{00 \ldots \ldots \ldots 00}^{n \text{ zeros}}$. 10^{-n} is just $1/10^n$, that is, a decimal fraction given by one unit in the nth decimal position.

responding nerve endings. Both sections of the cochlea are connected at the far end, or apex, by a small hole in the basilar membrane called helicotrema (Fig. 2.6b). They are filled with an incompressible fluid, the *perilymph.*[3] The lower section is sealed off with another elastic membrane at the round window.

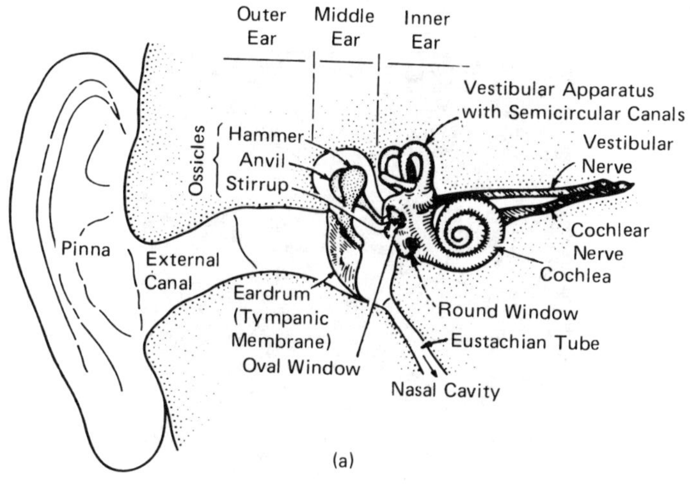

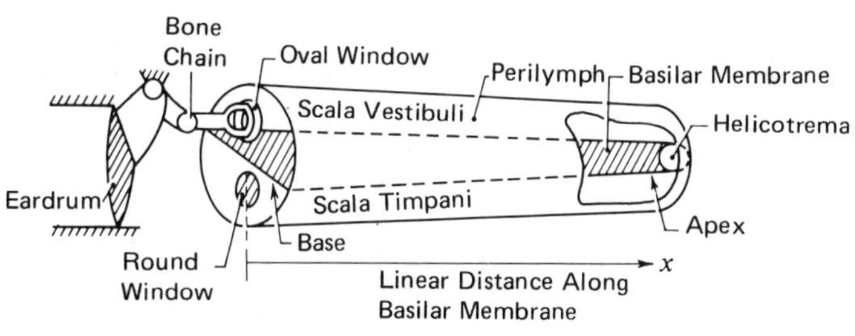

Fig. 2.6. (*a*) Schematic view of the ear (Flanagan 1972, Fig. 4) (not in scale); (*b*) the cochlea shown stretched out (highly simplified).

The vibrations transmitted by the bone chain to the oval window membrane are converted into oscillations of the perilymph fluid. These

---

[3] This is a highly oversimplified description. In reality, the cochlear partition is highly structured, including a channel (the scala media) filled with the endolymphatic liquid, bound by the basilar membrane in the lower part and by Reissner's membrane in the upper part. Another membrane (tectorial membrane) "floats" on top of the basilar membrane and plays a key role in the actual stimulation process.

oscillations propagate through the cochlear duct, and the basilar membrane is set into motion like a waving flag. About 30,000 receptor units, called *hair cells,* arranged in "inner" and "outer" rows along the basilar membrane (Fig. 2.7) (Bredberg et al. 1970) pick up the motions of the latter and impart signals to the nerve cells, or *neurons,* that are in contact with them (Spoendlin 1970).

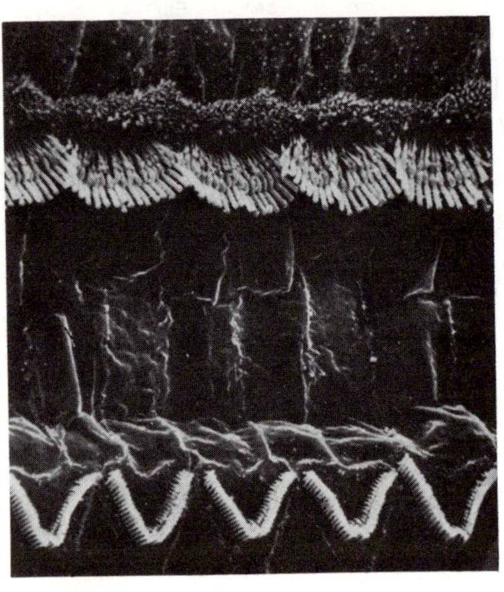

Fig. 2.7. Scanning electron micrograph (Bredberg et al. 1970) of the inner row (top) and outer row (bottom—only one of three rows is shown) of hair cells on the basilar membrane of a guinea pig. Copyright 1970 by the American Association for the Advancement of Science.

The remarkable fact is that for a pure sound of given frequency, the maximum basilar membrane oscillations occur only in a given, limited region of the membrane, *whose position depends on the frequency of the tone.* In other words, for each frequency there is a region of maximum sensitivity, or "resonance region," on the basilar membrane. The lower the frequency of the tone, the closer to the apex (Fig. 2.6b) lies the region of activated hair cells (where the membrane is most flexible). The higher the frequency, the closer to the entrance (oval window) it is located (where the membrane is stiffest). *The spatial position x along the basilar membrane* (Fig. 2.6b) *of the responding hair cells and associated neurons determines the primary sensation of pitch.* A change in frequency of the pure tone causes a shift of the position of the activated region; this shift is then interpreted as a change in pitch. We say that the primary information on tone frequency is "coded" by the sensorial organ of the basilar membrane in the form of *spatial location* of the activated neurons. Depending on which group of neurons is activated, the pitch will appear to us as low or high.

Fig. 2.8 shows how the position x (measured from the base, Fig. 2.6b) of the region of maximum sensitivity varies with the frequency of a pure, sinusoidal tone, for an average adult person (von Békésy 1960). Several important conclusions can be drawn. First of all, note that the musically most important range of frequencies (approximately 20–4,000 Hz) covers roughly two-thirds of the extension of the basilar

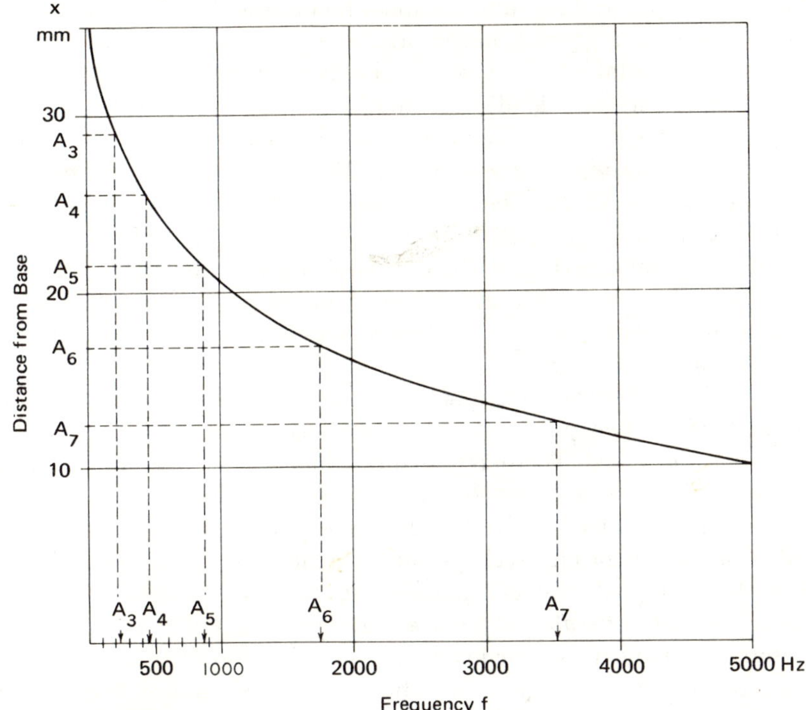

Fig. 2.8. Position of the resonance maximum on the basilar membrane (after von Békésy 1960) for a pure tone of frequency f (linear scales).

membrane (12–35 mm from the base). The large remaining portion of the frequency scale (4,000–16,000 Hz, not shown beyond 5,000 Hz in Fig. 2.8) is squeezed into the remaining one-third. Second, notice the significant fact that whenever the frequency of a tone is doubled, i.e., the pitch jumps one octave, the corresponding resonance region is displaced by a roughly constant amount of 3.5–4 mm, no matter whether this frequency jump is from 220 to 440 Hz, from 1,760 to 3,520 Hz, or, as a matter of fact, from 5,000 to 10,000 Hz. In general, whenever the frequency f is multiplied by a given factor, the position x of the resonance region is not multiplied but simply shifted a certain amount. In other words, it is frequency *ratios*, not their differences, that determine the displacement of the resonance region along the basilar membrane. A relationship of this kind is called "logarithmic" (Section 3.4).

The above results come from physiological measurements (von Békésy 1960) that can be performed on anesthetized (i.e., unconscious), or even dead (but well preserved) animals and involve only physical measurements. We now consider the psychophysical magnitude pitch, associated to a pure tone of frequency f. In Section 1.4 we mentioned that a psychophysical magnitude cannot be measured in the same quantitative manner as a physical magnitude, such as frequency. Only a certain *order* can be established by the experiencing individual between two sensations of the same kind presented in immediate succession. Quantitative estimates are possible only after the brain somehow has been trained to perform the necessary operations (e.g., a child learning to estimate the size of the objects he sees)—and the results would have to be interpreted in a statistical way. Even an untrained subject can emit a judgment on whether "tone 2" is of higher, equal, or lower pitch than "tone 1," when both are presented in succession.[4] But will he be able to judge *how much*—e.g., twice, one-third, or ten times—higher or lower that pitch was?

Let us consider an individual's ability to establish a relative order of pitch when two pure tones (of the same intensity) are presented one after the other. There is a natural limit: when the difference in frequency between the two tones is too small, below a certain value, both tones are judged as having the same pitch. This is true with the order judgments for all psychophysical magnitudes: whenever the variation of an original physical stimulus lies within a certain "difference limen" or "*just noticeable difference*" (abbreviated "jnd"), the associated sensation is judged as remaining "the same"; as soon as the variation exceeds the jnd, a change in sensation is detected. Notice that the jnd relates to a *physical* magnitude (the stimulus), is measurable in the ordinary sense, and is expressed by a number.

The degree of sensitivity of the primary pitch perception mechanism to frequency changes, or *frequency resolution* capability, depends on the frequency, intensity, and duration of the tone in question—and on the suddenness of the frequency change. It varies greatly from person to person, is a function of musical training, and unfortunately, *depends considerably on the method of measurement employed.* Fig. 2.9 shows the average jnd in frequency for pure tones of constant intensity (80 decibels, Section 3.4), whose frequency was slowly and continuously modulated up and down (Zwicker, Flottorp, and Stevens 1957). This graph shows, for instance, that for a tone of 2,000 Hz a change of 10 Hz—i.e., of only 0.5%—already can be detected. This is a very small

---

[4] This, of course, implies a previous mutual agreement on what "higher" and "lower" pitch means.

22

fraction of a semitone! *Sudden* changes in frequency are detected with a considerably lower jnd—up to 30 times smaller than the values shown in Fig. 2.9 (Rakowski 1971). Frequency resolution becomes worse at low frequencies (e.g., 3% at 100 Hz in Fig. 2.9). It also decreases with decreasing tone duration, once the latter falls below about one-tenth of a second.

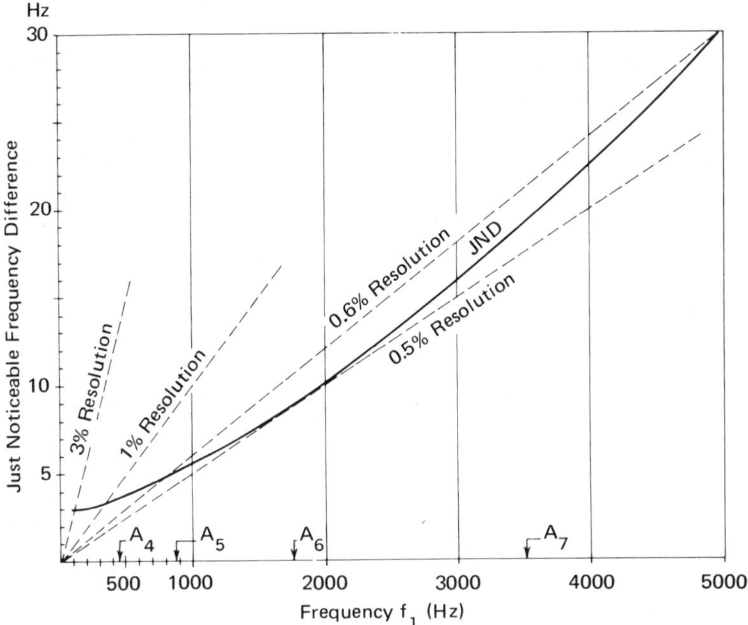

Fig. 2.9. Just noticeable difference in frequency for a pure tone of frequency f_1 (linear scales), as determined with a slowly frequency-modulated signal (after Zwicker, Flottorp, and Stevens 1957).

Apparently, the jnd in frequency (and, as a matter of fact, that of other physical stimuli) is not defined "sharply." Recent experiments (Stevens 1972) reveal that there are *two* critical threshold values: (1) a frequency increment *below* which a change in pitch is *never* detected, that has been called the "neural quantum" of pitch detection; and (2) a frequency increment *above* which a change of pitch is *always* detected, whose value is roughly twice that of the "neural quantum." Frequency changes of values *between* these two threshold values are *sometimes* detected, with a probability that increases linearly from 0 to 1. In the following discussion, however, we shall ignore this "fine structure" of the jnd.

Since the inception of psychophysics, psychologists have been tempted to consider the minimum perceptible change in sensation caused by a jnd of stimulus as the "natural" unit with which to "measure" the corresponding psychophysical magnitude. The minimum perceptible change in pitch has been used to construct a "subjective scale of pitch" (Stevens, Volkmann, and Newman 1937). However, since as we shall see later, the *octave* plays the overriding role of a "natural" pitch interval, and since all musical scales developed in total independence of the attempts to establish a subjective scale of pitch, the latter is only of marginal interest to music and will not be considered any further in this book.

In summary, according to the description given in this section, the primary function of the inner ear (cochlea) is to convert a vibration pattern in time (that of the eardrum) into a vibration pattern in space (that of the basilar membrane) and this, in turn, into a spatial pattern of neural activity. The theoretical description of this mechanism is called the *Place Theory of Hearing*. We shall come back to it quite frequently; we shall see that it is a good theory, but not a complete one. Another, more complicated pitch coding mechanism exists, operating in the nervous system.

2.4 Superposition of Pure Tones: First Order Beats and the Critical Band

We said before that single pure tones sound very dull. Things become a little livelier as soon as we superpose two pure tones by sounding them together. In this section we shall analyze the fundamental characteristics of the superposition of two pure tones. We will meet some very fundamental concepts of physics of music and psychoacoustics.

There are two kinds of superposition effects, depending on where they are processed in the listener's auditory system. If the processing is *mechanical,* occurring in the cochlear fluid and along the basilar membrane, we call them "first order superposition effects," mainly because they are clearly distinguishable and of fairly easy access to psychoacoustical experimentation. "Second order" superposition effects are the result of *neural* processing and are more difficult to detect, describe, and measure unambiguously. In this section we shall focus on first order effects only.

Let us first discuss the physical meaning of "superposition of sound." The eardrum moves in and out commanded by the pressure variations of the air in the auditory canal. If it is ordered to oscillate with a pure harmonic motion of given frequency and amplitude, we hear a pure tone of certain pitch and loudness. If now *two* pure tones of different characteristics are sounded together (e.g., by listening to two independent sources at the same time), the eardrum reacts as if it were executing at the same time two independent commands simultaneously, one given by each pure tone. The resulting motion is the sum of the individual motions that would occur if each pure sound were present alone, in the absence of the other. Not only the eardrum behaves this way, but also the medium and all other vibrating components (this, however, is not entirely true if the amplitudes are very large). This effect is called a *linear superposition* of two vibrations. Linear superposition of two vibrations is a technical term that means "peaceful coexistence": one component vibration does not interfere with the affairs of the other, and the resulting superposition simply follows the dictations from each component simultaneously. In a *non*linear superposition, the dictation from one component would depend on whatever the other one has to say, and vice versa.

We start our discussion with the analysis of the superposition of two simple harmonic motions with *equal frequency* and *equal phase* (zero phase difference, Section 2.2). It can be shown graphically (Fig. 2.10) and also analytically that in this case we again obtain a simple

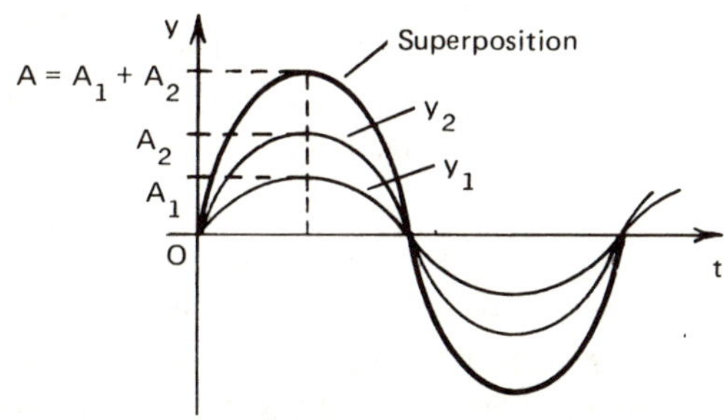

Fig. 2.10

harmonic motion of the same frequency, the same phase, but with an amplitude which is the sum of the amplitudes of the two component vibrations. If the two component oscillations of given frequency have *different phase*, their superposition still turns out to be a simple harmonic motion of the same frequency, but the amplitude will *not* be given anymore by the sum of the component amplitudes. In particular, if the amplitudes of the component vibrations are equal and their phase difference φ is 180°, both oscillations will annihilate each other and no sound at all will be heard. This is called *destructive interference* and plays a role in room acoustics. In summary, when two pure tones of equal frequency reach the eardrum, we perceive only *one* tone of given pitch (corresponding to the frequency of the component tones) and loudness (controlled by the amplitudes of the superposed tones and their phase difference).

We now consider the superposition of two simple tones of the same *amplitude* but with *slightly different frequencies*, f_1 and $f_2 = f_1 + \Delta f$. The frequency difference Δf has a small value. Let us assume that it is positive; the tone corresponding to f_2 is thus slightly sharper than that of f_1. The vibration pattern of the eardrum will be given by the sum of the pattern of each component tone (Fig. 2.11). The result of the superposition (heavy curve) is an oscillation of period and frequency *intermediate* between f_1 and f_2, and of slowly modulated amplitude. Note in this figure the slowly changing phase difference between the component tones y_1 and y_2: they start in phase (0° phase difference,

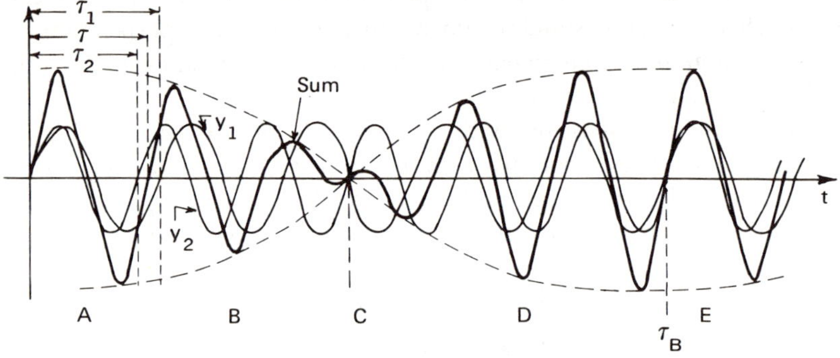

Fig. 2.11

as in Fig. 2.10) at the instant $t = 0$, then y_2 starts leading in phase (ahead of y_1) until both are completely out of phase (180° phase difference) at the instant corresponding to C. The phase difference keeps increasing until it reaches 360° = 0° at instant τ_B. This continuous, slow phase shift is responsible for the changing amplitude of the resultant oscillation: the broken curves in Fig. 2.11 represent the *amplitude envelope* of the resulting vibration (see also Fig. 2.17A).

What is the resulting tone sensation in this case? First of all, note very carefully that the eardrum will follow the oscillation as prescribed by the *heavy* curve in Fig. 2.11. The eardrum "does not know" and "does not care" about the fact that this pattern really is the result of the sum of two others. It has just *one* vibration pattern, of varying amplitude. A most remarkable thing happens in the cochlear fluid: this rather complicated, but single, vibration pattern at the oval window gives rise to *two* groups of traveling waves, one for each original component tone! *If the frequency difference Δf between the two component tones is large enough,* the corresponding resonance regions on the basilar membrane are sufficiently separated from each other; each one will oscillate with a frequency corresponding to the component tone (light curves in Fig. 2.11), and *we hear two separate tones of constant loudness,* with pitches corresponding to each one of the original tones. This property of the cochlea to disentangle a complex vibration pattern into the original pure tone components is called *frequency discrimination*. It is a mechanical process, controlled by the hydrodynamic and elastic properties of the inner ear constituents. On the other hand, *if the frequency difference Δf is smaller than a certain amount*, the resonance regions overlap, and *we hear only one tone of intermediate pitch with modulated or "beating" loudness.* In this case, the overlapping resonance region of the basilar membrane follows a vibration pattern essentially identical to that of the eardrum (heavy curve in Fig. 2.11). The amplitude modulation of the vibration pattern (envelope shown in Fig. 2.11) causes the perceived loudness modulation. We call this phenomenon "first order beats." These are the ordinary beats, well known to every musician.

The frequency of the resulting vibration pattern of two tones of very similar frequencies f_1 and f_2 is equal to the average value:

$$f = \frac{f_1 + f_2}{2} = f_1 + \frac{\Delta f}{2} \tag{2.2}$$

The time interval τ_B (Fig. 2.11), after which the resulting amplitude attains the initial value, is called the beat period. The beat frequency (number of amplitude changes per second) $f_B = 1/\tau_B$ turns out to be given by the difference:

$$f_B = f_2 - f_1 = \Delta f \tag{2.3}$$

It makes no difference whether f_2 is greater than f_1, or vice versa. Beats will be heard in either case, and their frequency will always be given by the frequency difference of the component tones (relation 2.3 really must be taken in *absolute value*, i.e., positive only). The closer together the frequencies f_1 and f_2 are, the "slower" the beats will result. If f_2 becomes equal to f_1, the beats disappear completely: both component tones sound in *unison.*

Let us summarize the tone sensations evoked by the superposition of two pure tones of equal amplitude and of frequencies f_1 and $f_2 = f_1 + \Delta f$, respectively. To that effect, let us assume that we hold f_1 steady and increase f_2 slowly from f_1 (unison, $\Delta f = 0$) to higher values. (Nothing would change qualitatively in what follows, if we were to decrease f_2.) At unison, we hear one single tone of pitch corresponding to f_1 and a loudness that will depend on the particular phase difference between the two simple tones. When we slightly increase the frequency f_2, we continue hearing *one* single tone, but of slightly *higher* pitch, corresponding to the average frequency $f = f_1 + \Delta f/2$ (2.2).[5] The loudness of this tone will be beating with a frequency Δf (2.3). These beats

---

[5] How do we verify that, indeed, the pitch sensation of the resulting tone *does* correspond to a tone of frequency $f_1 + \Delta f/2$? This is accomplished with *pitch matching* experiments: the subject is presented alternatively with a *reference* tone of controllable pitch and is requested to "zero in" the frequency of the latter until he senses "equal pitch" with respect to the original tone.

increase in frequency as f_2 moves away from f_1 (Δf increases). As long as Δf is less than about 10 Hz, these beats are perceived very clearly. When the frequency difference Δf exceeds, say, 15 Hz, the beat sensation disappears, giving way to a quite characteristic *roughness* or unpleasantness of the resulting tone sensation. When Δf surpasses the so-called *limit of frequency discrimination* Δf_D (not to be confused with the limen of frequency resolution, or jnd in frequency, of Fig. 2.9), we suddenly distinguish *two* separate tones, of pitches corresponding to f_1 and f_2. At that moment, both resonance regions on the basilar membrane have separated from each other sufficiently to give two distinct pitch signals. However, at that limit the sensation of roughness still persists, especially in the low pitch range. Only after surpassing a yet larger frequency difference Δf_{CB} called the *critical band,* the roughness sensation disappears, and both pure tones sound "smooth" and "pleasing." This transition from "roughness" to "smoothness" is in reality more gradual; the critical band as defined here only represents the *approximate* frequency separation at which this transition takes place.

All these results are easily verified using two electronic "sine-wave generators" of variable frequency whose output is combined and fed monaurally into each ear with headphones. But they can also be verified, at least qualitatively, with two flutes played simultaneously in the upper register by expert players. While one flautist maintains a fixed tone (holding the pitch very steady!), the other plays the same *written* note out of tune (pulling out or pushing in step by step the mouthpiece). Beats, roughness, and tone discrimination can be explored reasonably well.

Fig. 2.12 is an attempt (not in scale) to depict the above results comprehensively. The heavy lines represent the frequencies of tones (or beats) that are *actually* heard. Tone f_1 is that of fixed frequency, f_2 corresponds to the tone whose frequency is gradually changed (increased or decreased). The "fused" tone corresponds to the single tone sensation (of intermediate frequency) that is perceived as long as f_2 lies within the limit of frequency discrimination of f_1. Notice the extension of the critical band on either side of the unison ($\Delta f = 0$). We must emphasize again that this transition from roughness to smoothness is not at all sudden, as one might be tempted to conclude from Fig. 2.12, but rather gradual.

The limit for pitch discrimination and the critical band depend strongly on the average frequency $(f_1 + f_2)/2$ of the two tones (called the *center frequency* of the two-tone stimulus). They are relatively independent of amplitude, but may vary considerably from individual to individual. The critical band is related to several other psychoacoustical phenomena, and there are many (and, as a matter of fact, far more precise) ways to define it experimentally (Section 3.4). Fig. 2.13 shows the dependence of pitch discrimination Δf_D (Plomp 1964) and critical

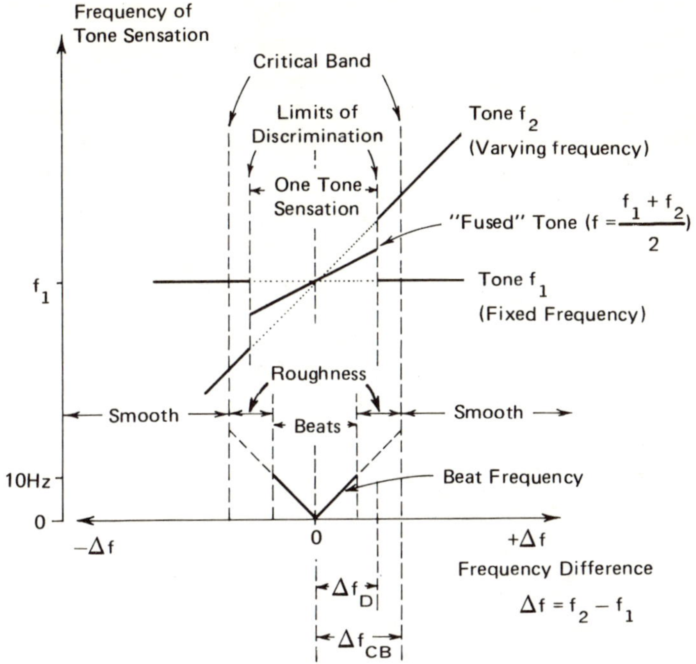

Fig. 2.12. Schematic representation of the frequency (heavy lines) corresponding to the tone sensations evoked by the superposition of two pure tones of nearby frequencies f_1 and $f_2 = f_1 + \Delta f$.

band Δf_{CB} (Zwicker, Flottorp, and Stevens 1957) with the center frequency of the component tones. For reference, the frequency differences that correspond to the musical intervals of a semitone, a whole tone, and a minor third are shown with broken lines. For instance, two tones in the neighborhood of 2,000 Hz must be at least 200 Hz apart to be discriminated, and more than 300 Hz apart to sound "smoothly." Note the remarkable fact that the limit of pitch discrimination is larger than a half-tone,[6] and even larger than a whole tone at both extremes of very high and very low frequencies. Note also the interesting fact that in the high pitch range, the critical band lies between the frequency difference that corresponds to a whole tone interval (qualified as a "dissonance") and that of a minor third (termed a "consonance")—i.e., roughly *extending over one-third of an octave*. In the lower frequency

---

[6] This may come as a surprise to musicians: they will claim that they can hear out very well the two component tones when a minor second is played on musical instruments! The point is this: the results shown in Fig. 2.13 only apply to *pure* tone superpositions, sounding *steadily* with constant intensity. When a musical interval is played with *real* instruments, the tones are not simple tones, they do not sound steadily, and a stereo effect is present. All this gives additional cues to the auditory system that are efficiently used for tone discrimination.

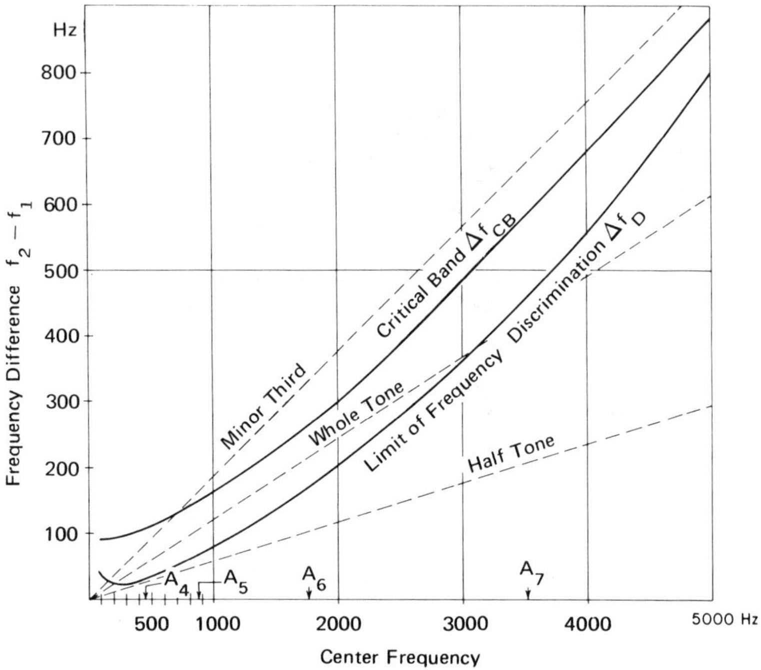

Fig. 2.13. Critical bandwidth Δf_{CB} (after Zwicker, Flottorp, and Stevens 1957) and limit of frequency discrimination Δf_D (Plomp 1964) as a function of the center frequency of a two-tone stimulus (linear scales). The frequency difference corresponding to three musical intervals is shown for comparison.

range there is an important departure: frequency discrimination and critical band are larger than a minor third (and even a major third). This is why thirds in general are not used in the deep bass register.

Compare Fig. 2.13 with Fig. 2.9: the limit for frequency discrimination Δf_D is roughly 30 times larger than the jnd for frequency resolution. In other words, we can detect very minute frequency changes of one *single* pure tone, but it takes an appreciable frequency difference between *two* pure tones sounding simultaneously, to hear out each component separately.[7]

---

[7] There is an equivalent experiment that can be performed with the sense of *touch* to point out the difference between "resolution" and "discrimination." Ask somebody to touch the skin of your underarm for about one second on a fixed point with a pointed pencil *while you look away*. Then ask the person to repeat this at gradually displaced positions. It will require a certain small but finite minimum distance before you can tell that the position of touch has changed—this is the "jnd" for localization of a single touch sensation, or "touch resolution." Now ask the person to use two pencils and determine how far both touching points must be from each other before you can identify *two* touch sensations. This is the minimum distance for "touch discrimination," which turns out to be considerably larger than the jnd. Both touch resolution and discrimination vary along the different

What are the implications of these results for the theory of hearing? The existence of a finite limit for tone discrimination is an indication that *the activated region on the basilar membrane corresponding to a pure tone must have a finite spatial extension.* Otherwise, if it were perfectly "sharp," two superposed tones would always be heard as two separate tones as long as their frequencies differed from each other—no matter how small that difference—and no beat sensation would ever appear. Actually, the fact that the roughness sensation persists even beyond the discrimination limit, is an indication that the two activated regions still overlap or interact to a certain degree, at least until the critical band frequency difference is reached. An illustrative experiment is the following: feeding each one of the two tones f_1 and f_2 *binaurally* into a different ear, the primary beat or roughness sensation disappears at once, both tones can be discriminated even if the frequency difference is way below Δf_D, and their combined effect sounds "smooth" at all times! The moment we switch back to a monaural input, the beats or roughness come back. Of course, what happens in the binaural case is that there is only *one* activated region on each basilar membrane with no chance for overlapping signals in the cochlea;[8] hence no beats or roughness.

At this stage the reader may wonder: if the region activated on the basilar membrane by *one* pure tone of *one* frequency is spatially spread, covering a certain finite range Δx along the membrane, how come we hear only *one* pitch and not a whole "smear" over all those pitches that would correspond to the different positions within Δx that have been activated? Unfortunately, we must defer the answer to the next chapter. Let us just anticipate here that a so-called *"sharpening"* process takes place after the signals from the stimulated region on the basilar membrane enter the neural network, in which the activity collected along the whole region Δx is "focused" or "funneled" into a very limited number of responding neurons that carry on the now well-defined primary pitch information to the brain. On the other hand, although extending over a finite range Δx, the vibrations of the membrane have all the same frequency in this case—that of the original pure tone. As we shall see in the next section, there is an additional pitch detection mechanism related to the neural coding of actual oscillations of the basilar membrane, that in this case may come as a "bonus" aid to the sharpening mechanism.

---

parts of the body. The equivalence between touch and hearing experiments is not at all casual: the basilar membrane is, from the point of view of biological evolution, a piece of skin with an enormously magnified "touch" sensitivity! This analogy has been profusely used by *von Békésy* (1960) in his superb experiments.

[8] There is, however, an overlap of *neural signals* in the upper stages of the neural pathway, giving rise to "second order" effects, to be discussed in Sections 2.6–8.

The beat phenomenon plays an important role in music. Whenever beats occur, they are processed by the brain giving us sensations that may range from displeasing or irritating to pleasing or soothing, depending on the beat frequency and the musical circumstances under which they appear. The peculiar, displeasing sound of an instrument out-of-tune with the accompaniment is caused by beats. The ugly sound of out-of-tune strings in a mediocre high-school orchestra is ugly in part because of the beats, and the "funny" sound of a saloon piano is caused by beats between out-of-tune pairs or triplets of strings in the middle and upper register. The fact that beats disappear completely when two tones have exactly the same frequency ($f_2 = f_1$) plays a key role for the process of *tuning* an instrument. If we want to adjust the frequency of a given tone to be exactly equal to the frequency of a given standard (e.g., a tuning fork) we do this by listening to beats and "zeroing in" the frequency until the beats have completely disappeared.[9]

The critical band, too, plays a key role in the perception of music. We shall discuss this concept in later sections in more detail. For the time being, let us just remark that the critical band represents a sort of "information collection and integration unit" on the basilar membrane. The experimental fact that the critical band frequency extension Δf_{CB} is roughly independent of sound amplitude or loudness is a strong indication that it must be related to some inherent property of the structure of the sensorial organ on the basilar membrane, rather than to the wave form in the cochlear fluid. One may convert the frequency extension Δf_{CB} shown in Fig. 2.13 into spatial extension along the basilar membrane by using Fig. 2.8: one obtains an almost constant value of about 1.2 mm for the critical band. Another, even more significant correlation is the following: the critical band turns out to correspond to an extension on the basilar membrane "serviced" by the roughly constant number of about 1,300 receptor cells (out of a total of about 30,000 on the membrane) (Zwislocki 1965), independently of the particular center frequency (i.e., position on the membrane) involved.

A complex auditory stimulus (e.g., from two pure tones) whose components are spread over a frequency extension that lies *within* the critical band causes a subjective sensation (e.g., roughness, in our example) that usually is quite different from a case in which the extension *exceeds* that of the critical band (smoothness in the two-tone example). This is true for a variety of phenomena. It plays an important role in the perception of tone quality (Section 4.8). Its effect on pure tone superposition provides the basis for a theory of consonance and dissonance of musical intervals (Section 5.2).

---

[9] In this chapter we have discussed the case of beats between *pure* tones only. As we shall see later, they similarly occur for the complex tones of real musical instruments.

2.5 Other First Order Effects: Combination Tones and Aural Harmonics

So far we have been analyzing the superposition effects of two pure tones whose frequencies were not too different from each other (Fig. 2.12). What happens with our tone sensations when the frequency of the variable tone, f_2, increases beyond the critical band, while f_1 is kept constant? The ensuing effects may be classified into two categories, depending on whether they originate in the ear or in the neural system, respectively. In this section we shall focus on a phenomenon belonging to the first category, the perception of *combination tones*. These tones are additional pitch sensations that appear when two pure tones of frequencies f_1 and f_2 are sounded together; they are most easily perceived if the latter are of high intensity level. These additional pitch sensations correspond to frequencies that differ from both f_1 and f_2, as can be established easily with pitch-matching or pitch-cancellation experiments (Goldstein 1970). *They are not present in the original sound stimulus*—they appear as the result of a so-called nonlinear distortion of the acoustical signal in the ear.

Let us repeat the experiment corresponding to Fig. 2.12 concerning the superposition of two pure tones, but this time turning up the loudness considerably and sweeping the frequency f_2 slowly up and down between the unison f_1 and the octave, of frequency $2f_1$. While we do this, we pay careful attention to the evoked pitch sensations. Of course, we will hear both the tone of constant pitch corresponding to the frequency f_1 and the variable tone f_2. But in addition, one clearly picks up one or more lower pitch tones sweeping up and down, depending on how we vary the frequency f_2. In particular, when f_2 sweeps upward away from f_1, we hear a tone of rising pitch starting from very deep. When f_2 sweeps downward starting at the octave $f_2 = 2f_1$, we also hear a tone of rising pitch starting from very deep. And paying even more attention, more than one low pitch tone may be heard at the same time. These tones, which do not exist at all in the original sound, are the combination tones.

The perhaps most easily identifiable combination tone at *high* intensity level is one whose frequency is given by the difference of the component frequencies:

$$f_{C1} = f_2 - f_1 \qquad (2.4)$$

It is also called the *difference tone*. Notice that for values of f_2 very close to f_1, f_{C1} is nothing but the beat frequency (2.3). f_{C1} must be at least 20–30 Hz to be heard as a tone. As f_2 rises, f_{C1} increases, too. When f_2 is an octave above f_1, $f_{C1} = 2f_1 - f_1 = f_1$—i.e., the difference tone coincides with the lower component f_1. When f_2 is halfway between f_1 and $2f_1$—

i.e., $f_2 = \frac{3}{2}f_1$ (a musical interval called the *fifth*)—the difference tone has a frequency $f_{C1} = \frac{3}{2}f_1 - f_1 = \frac{1}{2}f_1$, corresponding to a pitch one octave below that of f_1.

The two other combination tones that are most easily identified (Plomp 1965), *even at low intensity levels* of the original tones, correspond to the frequencies

$$f_{C2} = 2f_1 - f_2 \qquad (2.5)$$
$$f_{C3} = 3f_1 - 2f_2 \qquad (2.6)$$

Both tones f_{C2} and f_{C3} decrease in pitch when f_2 increases from unison toward the fifth, and they are most easily heard when f_2 lies between about $1.1f_1$ and $1.3f_1$. At high intensity of the original tones they also can be perceived quite well as low pitch sensations near the octave and the fifth, respectively. Note that the tones f_{C2} and f_{C1} coincide in frequency ($= \frac{1}{2}f_1$) when f_2 is at the fifth $\frac{3}{2}f_1$. In Fig. 2.14 we summarize

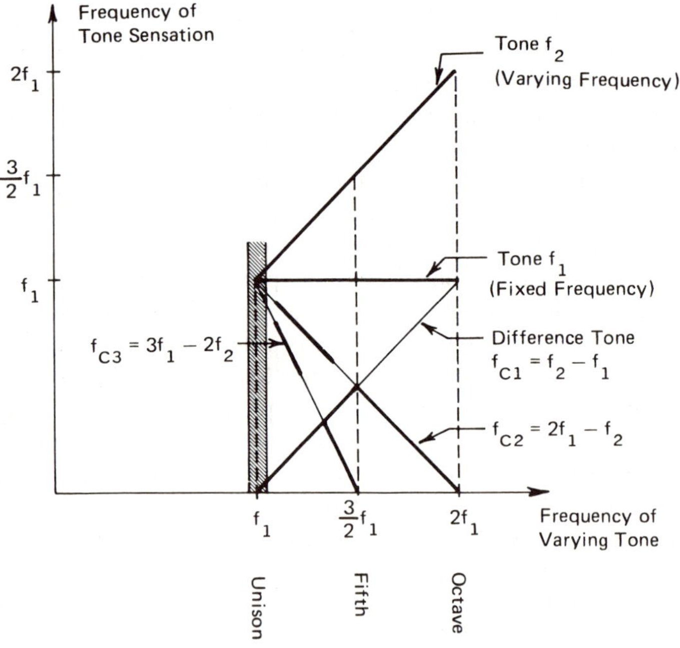

Fig. 2.14. Frequencies of the combination tones f_{C1}, f_{C2}, f_{C3}, evoked by a two-tone superposition (f_1, f_2). Heavy lines: most easily detected ranges of combination tones.

the first order tone sensations evoked by the superposition of two pure tones of frequency f_1 and f_2. Notice that Fig. 2.12 is nothing but a "close-up" picture of what happens when the frequency f_2 is very near f_1 (hatched area in Fig. 2.14). The portions of the combination tones shown with heavier track are the ones easiest to be heard out (the actual extent depends on intensity).

How are these exta tone sensations generated? As pointed out above, they are *not* present in the original sound vibration of the eardrum. Careful experiments conducted on animals have shown that combination tone frequencies are not even present at the entrance of the cochlea (oval window membrane, Fig. 2.6); on the other hand, from direct neural pulse measurements (Goldstein 1970) one must conclude that there *are* indeed activated regions on the basilar membrane at the positions corresponding to the frequencies of the combination tones. They are thought to be caused by a "nonlinear" distortion of the primary waveform stimulus in the cochlea. It can be shown mathematically that, indeed, when two harmonic (sinusoidal) oscillations of different frequencies f_1 and f_2 enter a transducer of distorted (nonlinear) response, the output will contain, in addition to the original frequencies f_1 and f_2, all linear combinations of the type $f_2 - f_1$, $2f_1 - f_2$, $3f_1 - 2f_2$, $f_2 + f_1$, $2f_2 + f_1$, etc.[10]) More recent experiments (Smoorenburg 1972) indicate that the difference tone (2.4) and the two other combination tones (2.5, 6) must originate in mutually independent cochlear mechanisms, respectively. The intensity threshold for the generation of the former is considerably higher than that of the latter, and roughly independent of the frequency ratio f_2/f_1.

It is interesting to note that even one *single* tone of frequency f_1 will give rise to additional pitch sensations when it is very loud. These additional tones, called *aural harmonics*, correspond to frequencies that are integer multiples of the original frequency: $2f_1$, $3f_1$, $4f_1$, etc.

Although all experiments pertinent to this section are most appropriately done with electronic tone generators, it is possible, at least qualitatively, to explore combination tones and aural harmonics using some musical instruments capable of emitting steady sounds at high intensity level. As a matter of fact, perhaps the most adequate "instrument" for this purpose is a dog whistle whose (high) pitch can be varied. A simple homemade experiment on combination tones can be done by blowing two such whistles at the same time—one at constant pitch, the other one sweeping the frequency away from and back to unison—and listening to low pitch tone sensations.

"Fake" combination tones can be easily generated in electronic organs and low quality hi-fi amplifiers and speakers. In these cases it is a nonlinear distortion in the electronic circuitry and mechanical system of the speaker that generates these parasitical frequencies. In particular, the difference tone can be produced and listened to quite clearly with an electronic organ: turn the loudness up, pull 8′ flute stops, play back

---

[10] It is not yet understood why the two last combinations do not appear as tone sensations.

and forth the sequence shown on the upper staff of Fig. 2.15, and listen for the low pitch tones indicated on the bottom staff:

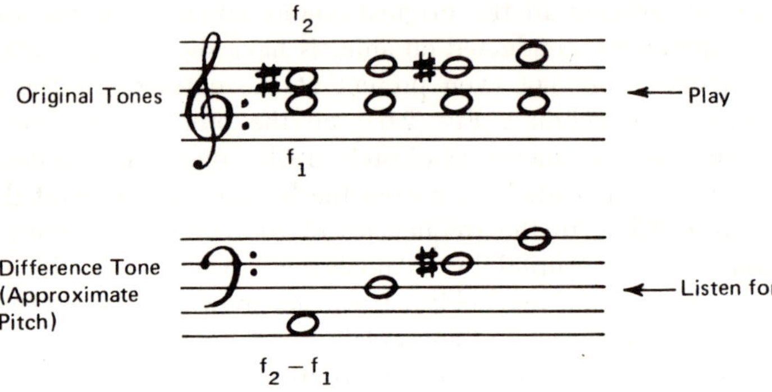

Fig. 2.15

Some of the difference tones thus generated are out of tune because of the equal-temperament tuning of the instrument (Section 5.5). We must point out again that what is heard in this experiment is a *fake* combination tone, in the sense that the low pitch sensation is generated in the speaker and *not* in the ear. It is quite clear from this example why electronic circuitry and speakers of hi-fi systems and electronic organs should have a "very" linear response. Concerning the role of "real" combination tones and aural harmonics, it is doubtful whether they play such an important role in music as it was believed until a few years ago.

2.6 Second Order Effects: Beats of Mistuned Consonances

We now repeat the experiment of the preceding section with two electronically generated pure tones, but this time ignoring possible combination tone sensations. We feed both tones at low intensity level into the same ear; tone f_1 is held at constant frequency, whereas f_2 can again be varied at liberty. The amplitudes of both pure tones are held constant throughout the experiment. When we sweep f_2 slowly upward, we notice something peculiar when we pass through the neighborhood of the octave $f_2 = 2f_1$: a distinct beating sensation, quite different from the "first order" beats near unison, but clearly noticeable. When f_2 is exactly equal to $2f_1$, this beat sensation disappears. It reappears as soon as we mistune the octave, i.e., when f_2 is set $f_2 = 2f_1 + \epsilon$, where ϵ (epsilon) represents only a few Hertz. The beat frequency turns out to be equal to ϵ. It is difficult to describe "what" is beating. Quite definitely, it is not loudness that is oscillating. Most people describe it as a beat in tone "quality." We call these *second order* beats; some prefer the name "subjective beats." They are the result of neural processing.

It is instructive to watch the vibration pattern on the oscilloscope while one listens to second order beats. This pattern is seen to change in exact synchronism with the beat sensations. Obviously, our auditory system must somehow be able to detect these changes of the *form* of a vibration pattern. Fig. 2.16 shows several vibration patterns cor-

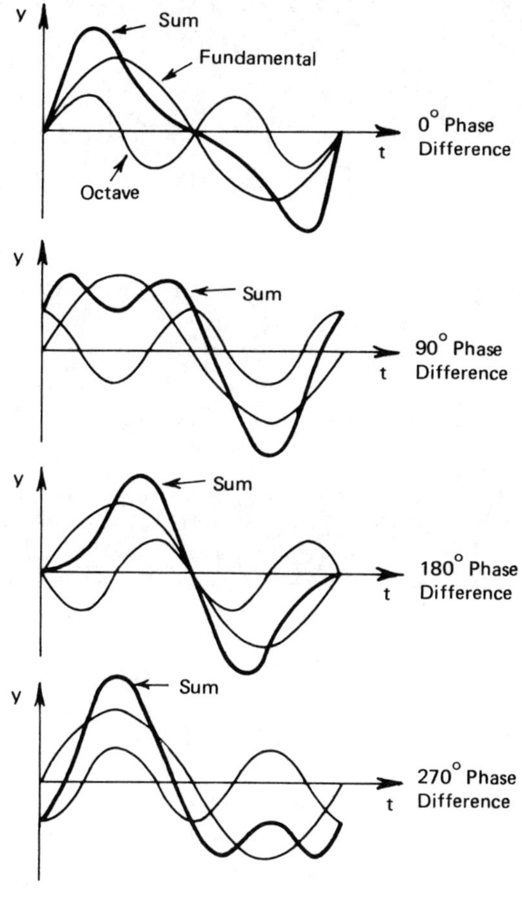

Fig. 2.16

responding to the superposition of a fundamental tone of frequency f_1 and its octave $f_2 = 2f_1$ (of smaller amplitude), for four different values of the phase difference. As long as the octave is perfectly in tune, the phase difference remains constant and the image on the oscilloscope static; any of the four superpositions sounds like the other—our ear does not distinguish one case from another. We say that the ear is insensitive to a static phase difference. But when we throw f_2 slightly out of tune: $f_2 = 2f_1 + \epsilon$, the mutual phase relationship will change continuously with time and the resulting vibration pattern will gradually undergo a shift from one of the forms shown in Fig. 2.16 to the next. It can be shown mathematically that this cycle of changing vibration pattern repeats with a frequency ϵ, the amount by which the upper

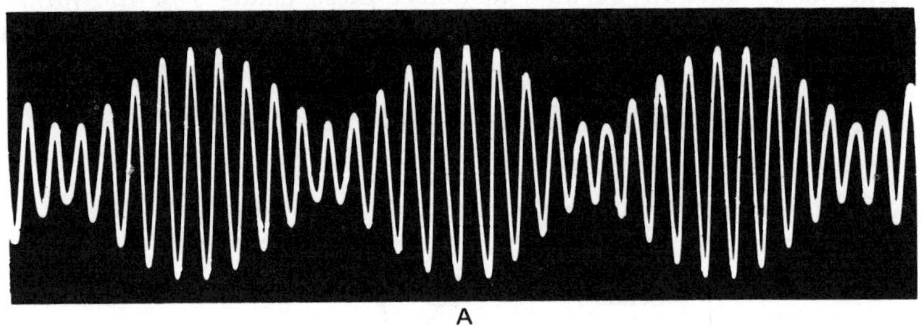

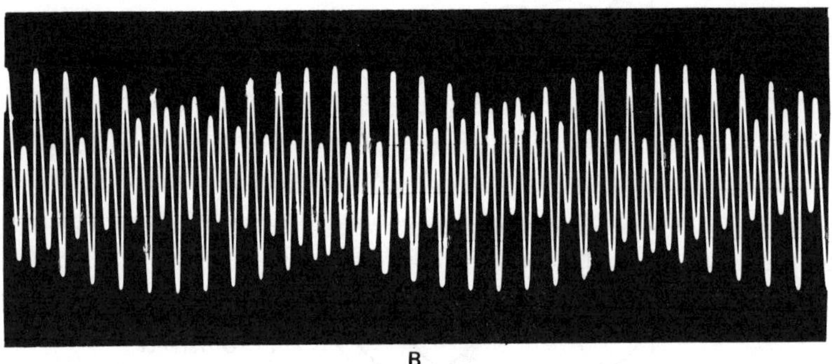

Fig. 2.17. Comparison of first order and second order beats. *Top:* first order beats (mistuned unison); amplitude modulation with no change in vibration pattern form. *Bottom:* second order beats (mistuned octave); pattern modulation with no change in total amplitude.

tone is out-of-tune from the octave. This obviously means that the ear is sensitive to a slowly changing phase difference between two tones.[11] An equivalent statement is: *the auditory system is capable of detecting cyclic changes in vibration pattern forms*. Notice carefully that there is no real change in amplitude from pattern to pattern in Fig. 2.16—quite contrary to what happens with first order beats, which are cyclic changes of vibration pattern amplitude (Fig. 2.11). Fig. 2.17 shows two actual oscilloscope pictures confronting first order beats near unison and second

---

[11] It is important not to confuse this type of phase sensitivity experiment with another kind in which a phase modulation of a high frequency tone is performed at a rate that lies in the audio range (Mathes and Miller 1947), way above a typical beat rate ϵ of less than 10–15 Hz.

38

order beats of a mistuned octave. Note the amplitude modulation of the former and the vibration pattern modulation in the latter. It is important to note that the second order beat sensation only appears in the low frequency range of the original two-tone stimulus. When f_1 (and f_2) exceeds about 1,500 Hz, second order beats cannot be perceived anymore (Plomp 1967).

Now we turn again to our experimental setup and explore the whole frequency range between unison and the octave. We discover that there are other pairs of values for f_2 and f_1, i.e., other musical intervals, in whose neighborhood beat sensations appear, though much less perceptible than for the octave. Two such "beat holes," as we may call them, can be found centered at the frequencies $f_2 = \frac{3}{2}f_1$ and $f_2 = \frac{4}{3}f_1$ corresponding to the musical intervals fifth and fourth, respectively. Again watching the vibration pattern on the oscilloscope at the same time as we listen, we realize that for a mistuned fifth ($f_2 = \frac{3}{2}f_1 + \epsilon$) and a mistuned fourth ($f_2 = \frac{4}{3}f_1 + \epsilon$), the vibration pattern form is not static (as happens with an exact fifth or fourth, i.e., for $\epsilon = 0$), but changes periodically in form (not in amplitude). The second order beats of the fifth are "faster" than those of the octave (for the fifth, the beat frequency is $f_B = 2\epsilon$, for the fourth $f_B = 3\epsilon$). This is not the only reason why they are more difficult to pick up: the vibration pattern itself gets more and more complicated (i.e., departs more and more from that of a simple harmonic motion) as we go from the octave (Fig. 2.16) to the fifth and to the fourth. The more complex a vibration pattern, the more difficult it is for the auditory system to detect its gradual change (Plomp 1967).

There is an optimal relationship between the intensities of the component tones for which second order beats are most pronounced, which always places the *higher pitch tone at a lower intensity* (Plomp 1967). Finally, it is important to note that second order beats are also perceived when the component tones are fed each one separately *into a different ear*.

Second order beats of mistuned consonances of *pure* tones do not play an important role in music (mainly because pure tones don't). But they are a crucial ingredient to the understanding of the processing mechanism of musical sound (Section 2.8).

2.7 Fundamental Tracking

We now introduce another series of psychoacoustical experiments that have been of crucial importance for the theories of acoustical perception. Let us consider two pure tones, a perfect fifth apart, of frequency f_1 and $f_2 = \frac{3}{2}f_1$. Fig. 2.18 shows the resulting vibration (sum) for one particular phase relationship. Notice that the pattern repeats exactly

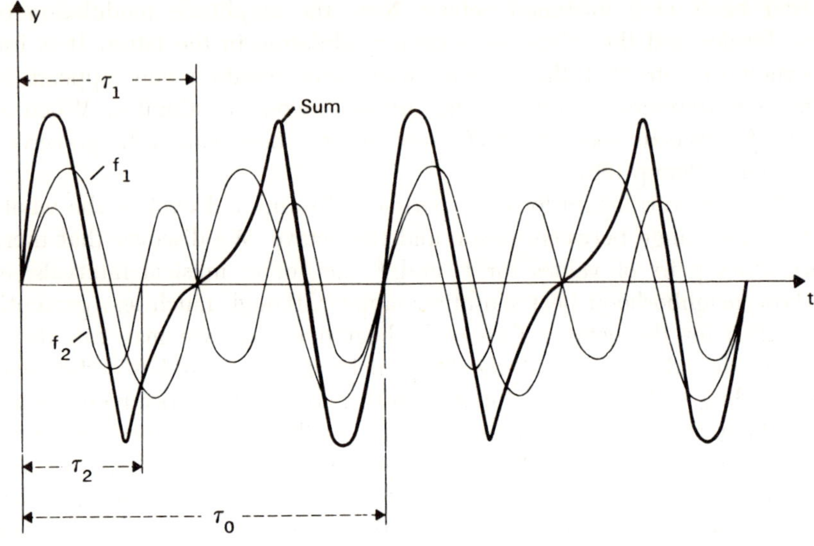

Fig. 2.18

in shape after a time τ_0 whch is twice as long as τ_1, the period of the lower pitch tone. This means that the *repetition rate* $f_0 = 1/\tau_0$ of the vibration pattern of a fifth is equal to one-half the lowest tone frequency:

$$f_0 = \tfrac{1}{2}f_1 \tag{2.7}$$

We call this repetition rate the "fundamental frequency" of the vibration. In this case, it lies one octave below f_1. *Our auditory system turns out to be sensitive to this repetition rate.* Indeed, if a short melody is played with this two-tone stimulus to a group of subjects, and they are asked to identify the subjective pitch sensation (the one-tone equivalent) associated with this melody, a majority will pick one that lies *one octave below* that of tone f_1.[12] Careful experiments have revealed that this is true even if the intensities of the two tones f_1 and f_2 are low, way below the threshold for combination tone production—a difference tone (which in this case also happens to have the same frequency $\tfrac{1}{2}f_1$) is thus ruled out (Plomp 1967). Actually, this effect has been used in music for many centuries (and wrongly attributed to a combination tone effect). For instance, since the end of the 16th century, many organs include a stop (the "5⅓-foot fifth") composed of pipes sounding a fifth higher than the pitch of the written note actually played. The

---

[12] Musically trained subjects usually first rebel at this experiment, either because they are disturbed by the "parallel fifths" in the melody, or because they will tend to focus on only one component of the original two-tone stimulus (f_1). But when told to carefully watch out for a pitch one octave below that of f_1, they suddenly discover that, indeed, it's there!

purpose is to simulate or reinforce the base *one octave below* the pitch of the written note (i.e., to reinforce the 16′ sound of the organ). Of even older usage is the 10⅔-foot fifth in the pedals which, in combination with 16′ stops, simulates or reinforces the 32′ bass (two octaves below the written note).

The tone of frequency f_0 (2.7) is not present as an original component. This tone is also called the *"missing fundamental"* (for reasons that will become apparent below); the corresponding pitch sensation is called *periodicity pitch* or *subjective pitch*. Experiments have shown that, for "normal" loudness levels, this frequency is *not* present in the cochlear fluid oscillations, either (whereas combination tones are). Indeed, the region of the basilar membrane corresponding to the frequency f_0 (Fig. 2.8) may be saturated (masked) with a band of noise (sound of an infinite number of component frequencies lying within a given range) so that any additional excitation of that region would pass unnoticed—yet the missing fundamental will still be heard (Small 1970). Or one may introduce an extra tone slightly out of tune with f_0; first order beats should appear if the missing fundamental tone f_0 did really exist in the cochlea—yet no beat sensation is felt. A more drastic effect is that the missing fundamental is perceived even if the two component tones are fed in dichotically, one into each ear (Houtsma and Goldstein 1971, 1972). All this is an indication that the missing fundamental, or periodicity pitch, must be the result of neural processing. It is another example showing that somehow our brain is capable of extracting information on the details of the vibration pattern—the repetition rate, in this case.

If we consider two tones forming a fourth, it can be easily shown by plotting the corresponding vibration pattern that the basic repetition rate is now

$$f_0 = \tfrac{1}{3}f_1 \tag{2.8}$$

i.e., a twelfth below the lowest tone. For the major third, $f_2 = \tfrac{5}{4}f_1$, the repetition rate is two octaves below f_1

$$f_0 = \tfrac{1}{4}f_1 \tag{2.9}$$

Again, in many organs there is a stop sounding a third above the written note. This reinforces the pitch *two* octaves below.

Note that the repetition rates corresponding to these musical intervals are identical to the frequencies of the corresponding difference tones (e.g., see 1st, 2nd, and 4th cases in Fig. 2.15). This is the reason why until only quite recently, the subjective pitch sensations (2.7, 8 and 9) were believed to be caused by difference tones. Subjective pitch detection, i.e., the capability of our auditory system to identify the repetition rate of the incoming, unanalyzed vibration pattern, only works in the lower (but musically most important) frequency range, below

about 1,500 Hz. The more complex the vibration pattern, i.e., the smaller
the interval between the component tones, the more difficult it is for
the auditory system to identify the repetition rate, i.e., the more difficult
it is to perceive subjective pitch.

Let us now "turn around" relations 2.7–9 and find out which pairs
of pure tone frequencies give rise to the *same* repetition rate or funda-
mental frequency f_0. We obtain:

$2f_0$ and $3f_0$	$3f_0$ and $4f_0$	$4f_0$ and $5f_0$	$5f_0$ and $6f_0$; etc.
fifth	fourth	major third	minor third

In other words, if f_0 corresponds to the note shown on the lower staff
in Fig. 2.19, the musical intervals shown in the upper staff yield that

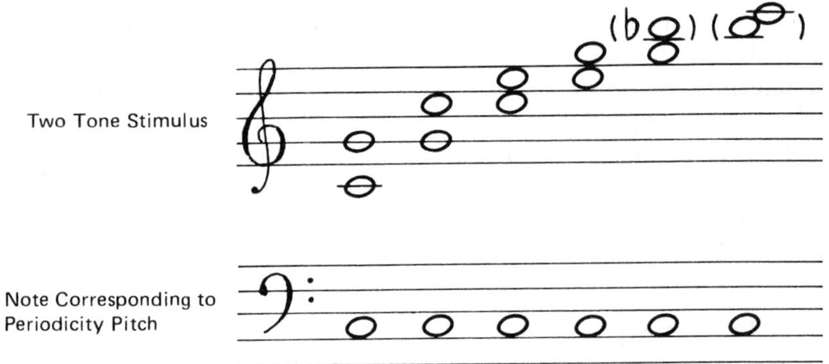

Fig. 2.19. Two-tone stimuli (upper staff) that give rise to the same
periodicity pitch (lower staff). The *B*-flat marked between parenthesis must
be tuned flat to yield a *C* as periodicity pitch.

same note as a subjective pitch sensation.[13] It is important to think of
the notes in Fig. 2.19 as representing *pure* tones of just one frequency
each, not as tones from real musical instruments. The individual compo-
nents of frequency $2f_0$, $3f_0$, $4f_0$, $5f_0$, ... etc. are called the *upper har-
monics* of the fundamental frequency f_0. Upper harmonic frequencies
are integer multiples of the fundamental frequency. Any two successive
tones of the upper harmonic series form a pair with the *same* repetition
rate or fundamental frequency f_0. Therefore, all upper harmonics, if
sounded together, will produce one single subjective pitch sensation
corresponding to f_0—*even if that latter frequency is totally absent in
the multi-tone stimulus!* This is the reason why the fundamental fre-

---

[13] Due to the tempered tuning of all musical instruments (Section 5.5), there
are slight variations of the actual frequency f_0 from case to case shown in Fig.
2.19. The *B* flat in the last two pairs should be tuned considerably flat, to yield
a *C* as subjective pitch.

42

quency corresponding to the subjective pitch, given by the repetition rate, has also been called the "missing fundamental," and why the perception of this repetition rate is called *fundamental tracking*. Note once more the striking property of this set of pure tones of frequencies $2f_0$, $3f_0$, $4f_0$, ... nf_0 . . . . . . : out of the infinite variety of possible pure-tone superpositions, this is the only one whose components, taken in pairs of consecutive tones, yield one and the same repetition rate.

If instead of considering consecutive tones, we would pick two arbitrary components, say, $4f_0$ and $6f_0$, the associated repetition rate $(2f_0)$, although different from the fundamental frequency f_0, still is a member of the family. In other words *any* two components of the harmonic series lead to repetition rates that still belong to that same series. In an *inharmonic* superposition of pure tones (one whose component frequencies are *not* integer multiples of a fundamental frequency) a whole "smear" of extraneous, parasitical, repetition rates appears. Since "real" musical tones happen to be made up of a superposition of harmonics (Chapter 4), *fundamental tracking is the auditory mechanism that enables us to assign a unique pitch sensation to the complex tone of a musical instrument* (Plomp 1967a).[14]

Finally, it is important to analyze what happens with the missing fundamental, i.e., the repetition rate, when the musical intervals are set out-of-tune. For instance, consider a mistuned fifth, of frequency $f_2 = \frac{3}{2}f_1 + \epsilon$. Plotting the resulting vibration pattern, one may realize easily that the actual pattern is repeated after a period τ_0 which is the *average* of $2\tau_1$ and $3\tau_2$. It can be shown mathematically that, for small values of the mistuning ϵ, the associated repetition rate f_0 is given by $f_0 = f_1/2 + \epsilon/6$. On similar grounds, for a mistuned fourth and a major third we obtain $f_0 = f_1/3 + \epsilon/8$, and $f_0 = f_1/4 + \epsilon/10$, respectively. It is interesting to compare these expressions with the frequencies of *difference* tones corresponding to the same mistuned consonances: $f_{C1} = f_1/2 + \epsilon$ (mistuned fifth); $f_{C2} = f_1/3 + \epsilon$ (mistuned fourth); $f_{C3} = f_1/4 + \epsilon$ (mistuned major third). Note that *difference tones get out of tune much more markedly than missing fundamentals*, for a given value of mistuning ϵ (the former are all proportional to ϵ, whereas the latter vary as the considerably smaller quantities $\epsilon/6$, $\epsilon/8$, $\epsilon/10$). In other words, subjective pitch is rather insensitive to the mistuning of the original tone interval.[15]

---

[14] The perhaps most convincing example of fundamental tracking of complex tones is given by the fact that one still is able to perceive the correct pitch of bass tones from a cheap transistor radio *in spite* of all frequencies below 100–150 Hz being cut off by the inadequate electronic circuitry and speaker!

[15] Without this property, it would be difficult for our auditory system to assign a well-defined subjective pitch to piano tones. Indeed, as we shall see in Chapter 4, the overtones of a piano string oscillation are all slightly out of tune (increasingly too sharp), but due to the "attenuation" of the amount of mistuning by the factors $\frac{1}{6}$, $\frac{1}{8}$, $\frac{1}{10}$, etc., with which ϵ is multiplied, the repetition rate of the complex tone is hardly affected. The same is true for the slightly inharmonic overtones of many other instruments.

2.8 Periodicity Pitch and The Theory of Hearing

The discovery of second order effects in auditory processing, such as the perception of phase changes, beats of mistuned consonances and fundamental tracking, has had a great impact on the theory of hearing. Indeed, these effects cannot be explained appropriately with the conventional "place theory" (Section 2.3). This does not mean, though, that this latter theory is wrong—it simply means that it has to be expanded or implemented. According to the discussion in Section 2.4, the auditory system should get little if any information on the "shape" of the full vibration pattern when two tones an octave or a fifth apart are sounded together. The two activated regions on the basilar membrane corresponding to these two component tones apparently would be too far away from each other to interact. The fact that the neural system *does* get information clues on the full, unanalyzed, original vibration pattern means that sufficient overlap between both resonance regions still must exist even if both tones are an octave apart, and that the nervous system is able to extract information from it. From the point of view of cochlear hydrodynamics, careful measurements on well-preserved animal cochleas have indeed revealed that an appreciable portion of the basilar membrane, extending beyond the critical band, is mechanically activated by a single pure tone, with a maximum located at the position given by Fig. 2.8, falling off steeply toward the helicotrema (Fig. 2.6) and flatter toward the oval window (von Békésy 1960).

Another significant fact is related to the arrangement of the actual receptor units on the basilar membrane. These sensor units or hair cells are grouped in "internal" and "external" rows that run along the basilar membrane from the base to the apex (Fig. 2.7). Nerve endings making contact with the hair cells receive orders from the latter to fire electrical impulses whenever the stimulus surpasses a given threshold. A most significant feature is the arrangement of these nerve endings. While a single nerve fiber usually contacts only 2–4 neighboring sensor units of the *inner* row of hair cells, thus receiving messages from a spatially very limited region, single nerve fibers innervating the *outer* rows make contact with sensor units that may lie several millimeters from each other (Davis 1962), thus being able to collect simultaneous information from over a wider range of frequencies. These outer hair cells seem to be more sensitive to a given acoustic stimulus (lower threshold) than those of the inner row.[16]

All this suggests that both groups of hair cells play quite distinct roles in auditory detection. In particular, the inner row seems mainly suited for primary pitch (and intensity) determination (Section 2.3),

---

[16] Recent studies seem to indicate, though, that the great majority of sensory neurons is associated with the inner hair cells (Spoendlin 1970).

whereas the outer hair cells seem designed to collect the information needed for a detailed vibration pattern analysis (i.e., second order beats, subjective pitch). It is significant that only higher mammals possess *two* types of rows of hair cells.

A complicating factor arises from the fact that, as discussed in Sections 2.6 and 2.7, beats of mistuned consonances and periodicity pitch can be perceived even if each component tone is fed dichotically to a different ear. In such a case, of course, the complete vibration pattern never arises—what must arise is a superposition or interaction of the neural signals from both cochleas *after* they have been combined at the medullar or midbrain levels. The result of this neural superposition should then be equivalent to the signals triggered by the more complex pattern of a superposition of tones in the original sound stimulus.

In summary, evidence seems to confirm that the auditory neural system does receive information on the details of the full, unanalyzed vibration pattern. How is this actually accomplished, how is this information actually coded, that is, converted into nerve impulses? In order to deal with this problem, we must first briefly examine in general terms the transmission of neural messages (Eccles 1970).

The fundamental processing and transmission unit of the neural system is the nerve cell or *neuron*. A typical neuron is shown in Fig. 2.20. One distinguishes the cell *body*, a series of ramified processes called *dendrites*, and an elongated fiber, the *axon*, which also may split into multiple branches. The dendrites and the cell body are the *receptors* of incoming neural signals, and the axon is the *effector*, passing them on to other neurons. These neural signals consist of electrical impulses (electric voltage variations) of several tens of millivolts. These impulses can be registered by implanting microelectrodes into the neuron (a procedure which does not affect the normal function of the cell). In the axon each impulse, called action potential, has nearly the same shape and duration (several tenths of milliseconds), and travels from the cell body to the axon endings. The fundamental neural message is given by the *rate and the distribution in time* with which individual impulses are fired along the axon.

The axon is "wired" to dendrites or cell bodies of other neurons. The contact points are called *synapses*. One given axon may be in synaptic contact with many other cells; conversely, one given cell may be wired to incoming axons from hundreds of other cells.[17] An impulse arriving at a synaptic contact causes the release of a chemical substance from the presynaptic cell into the space between both cell membranes (synaptic cleft). The presence of this substance triggers an electrical impulse in the postsynaptic cell, the "synaptic potential." Synaptic poten-

---

[17] Exceptions are the unipolar neurons whose single dendrites form the afferent nerve fibers.

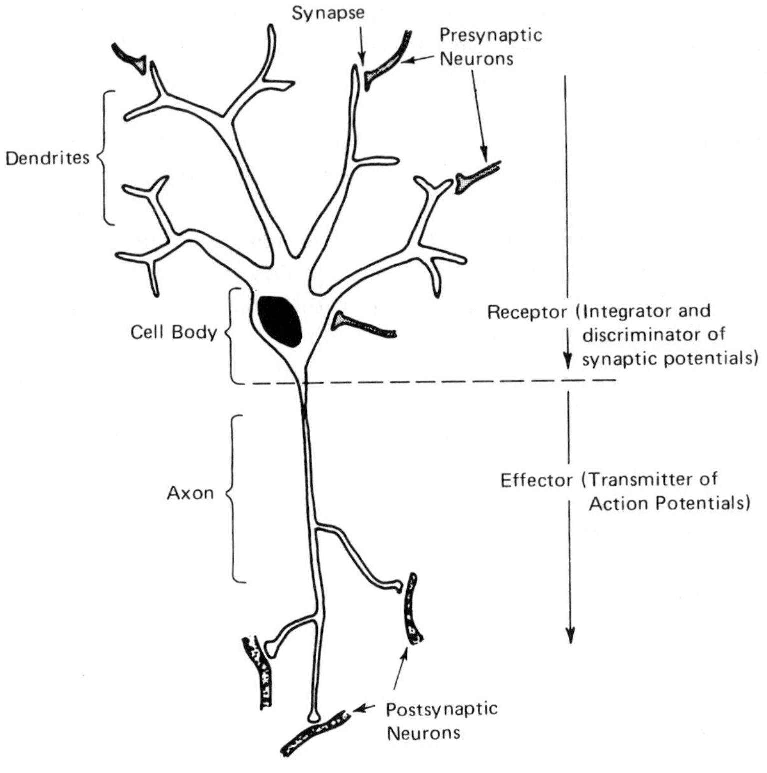

Fig. 2.20

tials are of varying shape and of longer duration than the standard-sized action potentials that propagate through the axon. There are two distinct types of synapses, *excitatory* and *inhibitory,* evoking synaptic potentials of mutually opposite polarity. If a neuron receives at a given instant of time a number of excitatory stimulations that exceeds the number of simultaneously arriving inhibitory signals by a certain threshold value, it will respond by firing an impulse into its axon. Otherwise it will remain silent. We conclude that the dendrites and their synapses function as the information collection and integration system of the neuron—thus representing the fundamental information-processing unit in the nervous system. One given neuron only imparts either excitatory or inhibitory orders to other neurons, but never both kinds. An inhibitory neuron firing a pulse to another inhibitory neuron will *cancel* the inhibitory effect of the latter.

There is a characteristic time delay (typically less than a millisecond) between the arrival of an impulse to a synapse and the formation of the response in the postsynaptic cell. This time delay makes it possible that neural activation triggered by one single external stimulus may subsist or "reverberate" for a considerable amount of time, when it propagates through a serial relay of thousands of successive synaptic steps in the cerebral tissue. This may be a key process in the buildup of time dependent patterns of neural activity (e.g., Section 4.8). After each activation, a neuron has a refractory period during which it cannot be reexcited, or during which its firing threshold is increased. One single neuron is just a "microscopic" component of a conglomerate of about 10 billion neurons in the human brain. It is in the "wiring scheme" among these 10 billion neurons where the "secret" of intelligence, behavior, feelings, and fears of human beings lies buried. In a broad macroscopic sense, the development of this wiring scheme is commanded by the genetic code of the species (although a high degree of randomness is always present at the microscopic, neuron-to-neuron, level). However, in an important part of the neural system, especially in the cerebral cortex, the particular distribution of firing thresholds is the result of repetitive action of stimulation patterns—in other words, of experience and learning.

When an individual neuron of the neural tract pertaining to a given sense organ is observed with a microelectrode, one in general finds a correlation of the firing rate with the magnitude of certain physical parameters of the original stimulus. Individual firings usually do not occur regularly spaced at equal time intervals—they appear distributed statistically at random. It is their *average* rate that counts (however, see further below). A neuron may be found to be firing even in absence of the original stimulus; this is called *spontaneous activity* and may happen at average rates up to several tens of Hertz in the peripheral neurons. For such a neuron it is the *change* in firing rate (increase *or* inhibition) that constitutes the elementary neural message. A persisting constant stimulus will in general evoke a firing rate that gradually decreases with time until it levels off at a certain lower value. This phenomenon is called *adaptation.* Some neurons, on the other hand, are found to respond only to *time changes* of stimuli, others to a whole complex of particular spatial configurations or time patterns of the stimulus (*feature detectors*). As a general rule, the higher up we move along the neural pathway from the receptors to the brain cortex, the more complex and elaborate will be the stimulus features to which a given neuron responds.

We are now in a better position to discuss how the neural system may collect and code information on the vibration pattern. When the acoustical signal of a single pure tone of given frequency arrives at the ear, the basilar membrane oscillations stimulate the hair cells that lie in the resonance region corresponding to that frequency (Section 2.3). It has been found by implanting microelectrodes in acoustically activated cochlear nerve fibers, that these increase their firing rate only during that part of the vibration cycle *in which the basilar membrane is moving in an upward direction* (Whitfield 1970), corresponding to an outward direction of motion of the eardrum (pressure rarefaction in the meatus). Fig. 2.21 shows a hypothetical time distribution of neural impulses in a nerve fiber of the inner ear connected to the appropriate resonance region of the basilar membrane, when it is excited by a low frequency tone.

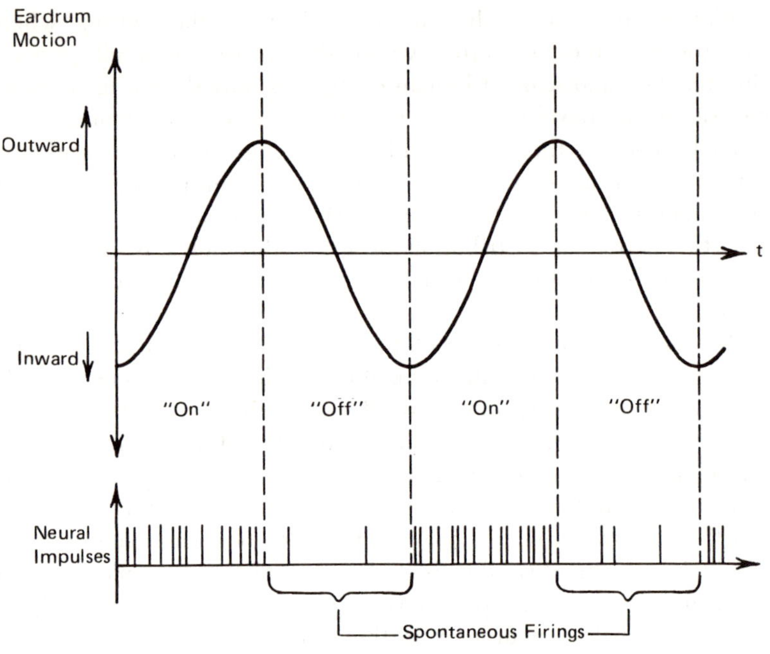

Fig. 2.21

An inspection of this figure reveals how information on repetition rate (actually, the repetition period) of the original acoustical signal can be coded in the form of "trains" of nerve impulses. Fig. 2.21 would correspond to an ideal case of extremely low frequency, though. Actually, the acoustical frequencies are usually higher than those of neural firing rates, and the *real* situation corresponds more to one in which the "on" and "off" intervals are much less clearly delineated due to their short duration (as compared to a typical neuron's refractory period) and to the random character of the impulse distribution. The only *statistically* important property is that there will be more impulses falling into "on" intervals than into "off" intervals. As a result, for pure tones, *the time interval between successive impulses will tend to be an integer multiple of the sound vibration period* τ (Kiang et al. 1965). It is clear that the higher the frequency of the tone, i.e., the shorter the duration of the "on" intervals, the less well-defined will be this grouping. For fre-

48

quencies above a few thousands of Hertz, it does not work at all. When several fibers receiving stimuli from a narrow region of the basilar membrane are bundled together (as it happens in the auditory nerve), the sum of their impulses (as detected by a macroelectrode that simultaneously makes contact with many fibers at the same time) will appear in synchronism with the auditory stimulus. These collective synchronous nerve signals have been called *volleys*.

In summary, a given fiber connected to the low frequency resonance region of the basilar membrane (near the apex) is capable of carrying two types of information: (1) the simple fact that *it is firing* tells the auditory system that the basilar membrane has been activated at or near the region innervated by that fiber—the spatial distribution (or "tonotopic" organization) of firing fibers thus codes the information on primary pitch ("Place Theory" of hearing). This process works for the whole range of frequencies. (2) The actual *time distribution* of impulses codes the information on repetition rate or periodicity pitch and, possibly also on details of the vibration pattern itself (see below). This only works in the lower frequency range. It is important to note that a given fiber has a maximum response to that acoustical frequency f which evokes a maximum excitation at the place x of the basilar membrane (Fig. 2.8) innervated by that fiber (this frequency for maximum response has been called the fiber's "best frequency"). On the other hand, a given fiber carries information on repetition rate (via the time distribution of its firing spikes) most efficiently if the stimulus frequency is considerably *lower* than the fiber's own "best frequency" (Simmons 1970).

We may invoke the effect shown in Fig. 2.21 to attempt an explanation of how information on the vibration pattern and its variations (second order beats) could be coded. Consider the superposition of two tones an octave apart. Assume that the resulting vibration pattern is that shown at the bottom of Fig. 2.16 and suppose that upward movements of the basilar membrane correspond to the positive direction of y. Two resonance regions will arise on the basilar membrane, centered at positions x_1 and x_2 corresponding to the two component frequencies f_1 and $f_2 = 2f_1$ (Fig. 2.8). In the cochlear nerve bundle we shall have two main foci of activity centered at the fibers whose "best frequencies" are f_1 and f_2, leading to two primary pitch sensations, one octave apart. However, as stated before, the resonance regions on the basilar membrane are rather broad, and there would be sufficient overlap on the region between x_1 and x_2 where the points of the membrane will vibrate according to a superposed pattern related to the original motion of the eardrum.[18] Fibers connected to that overlapping region will thus respond

---

[18] Traveling waves in the cochlear fluid change their phase relationship as they propagate, thus altering the *actual* form of the vibration pattern.

with firings that are grouped in "on" intervals which, say, correspond to the ascending (positive slope) portions of the bottom graph in Fig. 2.16. Note that, in this case, these "on" intervals are not of equal duration (as in the sinusoidal case of Fig. 2.21), but that they form an alternating "short-longer-short-longer" sequence. If the two tones were a fifth apart, the vibration pattern of the overlapping region could be that shown in Fig. 2.18, leading to a yet different type of sequence of "on" intervals. Periodicity of this sequence thus would represent the information on repetition rate, whereas structure of the sequence (a sort of "Morse code") would give information on the vibration pattern. Fig. 2.22 shows an example (a so-called histogram) of the distribution of time intervals between neural pulses in an auditory nerve fiber (Rose et al. 1969), for a stimulus corresponding to a musical fifth in a given phase relationship (see vibration pattern). Note the difference in the relative number of

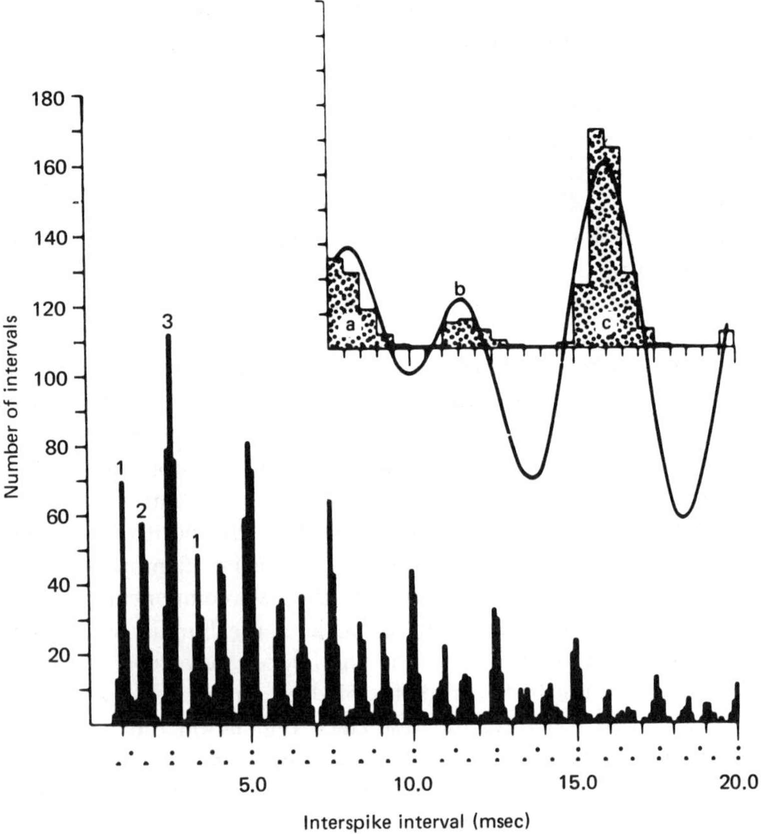

Fig. 2.22. A histogram showing the number of times (vertical axis) a given interval between neural spikes occurs (horizontal axis), in an auditory nerve fiber stimulated with a two-tone superposition (fifth). The vibration pattern is also shown (Rose et al. 1969). By permission from the authors.

times (vertical axis) a given interval between successive pulses (horizontal axis) appears. This represents the (statistical) "Morse code" mentioned above, carrying information on the vibration pattern. The greater the complexity of the original vibration pattern and the higher the frequency of the component tones, the more "blurred" the information conveyed by the pulse sequence will be, i.e., the more difficult to be interpreted at the higher brain centers.

This picture runs into complexities if one takes into account the established capability of the auditory system to determine the missing fundamental even if the two component tones are fed in dichotically (Houtsma and Goldstein 1971). In that case, indeed, each auditory nerve only carries information pertaining to a purely sinusoidal tone—of different frequency and phase, of course. Hence, the "Morse code" giving information on the (physically nonexisting) vibration pattern of the two-tone superposition must arise somehow *as a result of the interaction of the neural impulse distributions from both ears.* Such interactions are indeed possible either at the medullar or the midbrain level, where the nerve fiber decussations (cross-connections from both cochleas) occur.

Finally, we should say a few words on how the information on repetition rate and vibration pattern, initially coded in the form of the time distribution of neural impulses, might be recoded and interpreted by the brain. No direct experimental information is available on this mechanism; only *models* have been devised, based on possibilities (but not necessarily on realities) of the nervous system. One model is based on a process called *autocorrelation,* in which information on an incoming vibration cycle is intercompared with that pertaining to previous cycles; similar, repetitive features are enhanced and all others (nonperiodic) are discarded. A highly schematized neural model for this process is shown in Fig. 2.23 (Licklider 1959). Impulses traveling up along an axon A called "straight line" are intercompared with the same impulses that have been branched off into a neural "delay line" B (each synapse introduces an additional retardation and hence signals travel slower through the delay line than through the straight line). If the time distribution of the original signals has a certain periodicity, there will be coincident excitations at only *certain* endings of ascending fibers (those for which the delayed signals have fallen an integer number of periods behind the original signals). Assuming that *two* such excitations are simultaneously required to fire an ascending fiber, the location z (Fig. 2.23) of all activated neurons will bear information on vibration pattern characteristics, such as phase and repetition rate. In other words, the information on the vibration pattern (time distribution of impulses) has now been encoded in the simple form of a spatial distribution (z) of neural activity. Each ascending fiber (Fig. 2.23) is thus responsive to one given repetition rate, and one given distribution of activity in the z-dimension corresponds to a given pattern of vibration. Equivalent

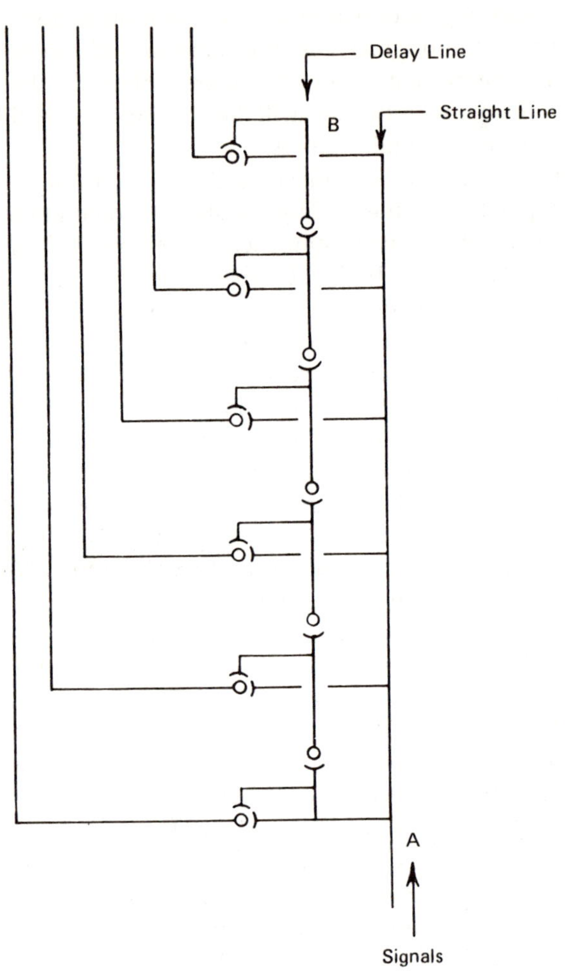

Fig. 2.23. Model for a neural crosscorrelation mechanism (repetition rate detector) (after Licklider 1959).

models can be devised invoking the action of inhibitory neurons (Whitfield 1970). It is not known at what level such a mechanism could actually be operative. The fact that second order effects are detected even if the tone components are fed into separate ears would place the autocorrelation process in some upper stage of the auditory neural pathway.

Neuronal models have also been devised to describe the process of *crosscorrelation* in which the time difference between the signals from both cochleas is determined, leading to the perception of sound directionality (binaural lateralization). Fig. 2.24 (Licklider 1959) de-

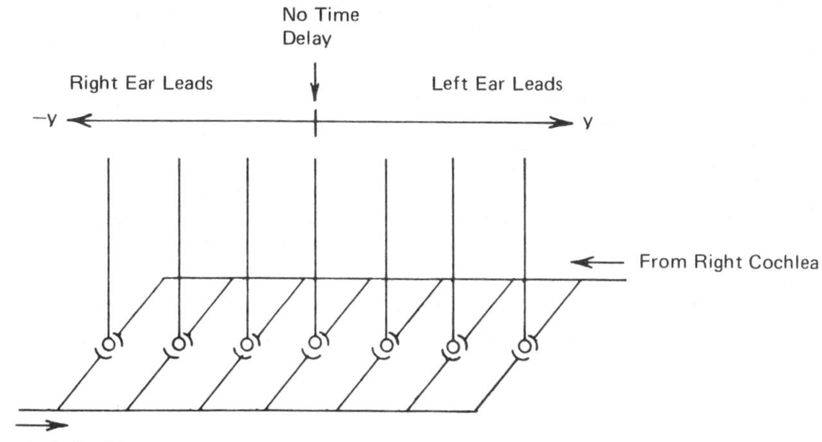

Fig. 2.24. Model for a neural autocorrelation mechanism (interaural time-difference detector) (after Licklider 1959).

picts a possible scheme. Here again it is assumed that an ascending neuron can fire only if it is excited simultaneously by both incoming fibers. Since a neural signal propagates with a finite velocity along a fiber, simultaneous arrival at a given ascending neuron ending requires a certain *time difference* between the original signals in both cochleas. For instance, exact simultaneity (zero time difference) of both cochlear signals would fire the ascending neuron located exactly in the middle, because that is the place where both right and left signals meet. If on the other hand the original signal is detected first in the *right* ear, its pulse will travel past the middle point until it meets the delayed pulse from the left ear. It is easy to see that the location y (Fig. 2.24) of the activated ascending neuron will depend on the interaural time delay, which in turn depends on the direction of the incoming sound. *Binaural fusion* is the process by means of which we are able to merge into one tonal image the input from both ears. It is equivalent to the effect of fusion into one three-dimensional image of the information from both eyes.

References

Bredberg, G., H. H. Lindemann, H. W. Ades, R. West, and H. Engström, 1970. Scanning electron microscopy of the organ of Corti. *Science* **170**:861.

Davis, H. 1962. Advances in the neurophysiology and neuroanatomy of the cochlea. *J. Acoust. Soc. Am.* **34**:1377.

Eccles, J. C. 1970. *Facing Reality.* Springer-Verlag, New York.

Flanagan, J. L. 1972. *Speech Analysis, Synthesis and Perception.* 2nd ed. Springer-Verlag, New York.

Goldstein, J. L. 1970. Aural combination tones. In *Frequency Analysis and Periodicity Detection in Hearing*. R. Plomp and G. F. Smoorenburg, eds. A. W. Suithoff, Leiden.

Houtsma, A. J. M., and J. L. Goldstein. 1971. Perception of musical intervals: evidence for the central origin of the pitch of complex tones. Massachusetts Institute of Technology, Research Laboratory of Electronics, Technical Report 484; 1972. *J. Acoust. Soc. Am.* **51**:520.

Kiang, N. Y.-S., T. Watanabe, E. C. Thomas, and L. F. Clark. 1965. *Discharge Patterns of Single Fibers in the Cat's Auditory Nerve*. M.I.T. Press, Cambridge, Mass.

Licklider, J. C. R. 1959. Three auditory theories. In *Psychology: a Study of a Science*. Vol. I. S. Koch, ed. McGraw Hill Book Company, New York.

Mathes, R. C., and R. L. Miller. 1947. Phase effects in monaural perception. *J. Acoust. Soc. Am.* **19**:780.

Plomp, R. 1964. The ear as a frequency analyzer. *J. Acoust. Soc. Am.* **36**:1628.

Plomp, R. 1965. Detectability threshold for combination tones. *J. Acoust. Soc. Am.* **37**:1110.

Plomp, R. 1967. Beats of mistuned consonances. *J. Acoust. Soc. Am.* **42**:462.

Plomp, R. 1967a. Pitch of complex tones. *J. Acoust. Soc. Am.* **41**:1526.

Rakowski, A. 1971. Pitch discrimination at the threshold of hearing. *Proc. Seventh Int. Congr. Acoust.*, Budapest.

Rose, J. E., J. F. Brugge, D. J. Anderson, and J. E. Hind. 1969. Some possible neural correlates of combination tones. *J. Neurophys.* 32, 402.

Simmons, F. B. 1970. Monaural processing. In *Foundations of Modern Auditory Theory*. J. V. Tobias, ed. Academic Press, New York.

Small, A. M. 1970. Periodicity pitch. In *Foundations of Modern Auditory Theory*. J. V. Tobias, ed. Academic Press, New York.

Smoorenburg, G. F. 1972. Audibility region of combination tones. *J. Acoust. Soc. Am.* **52**:603.

Spoendlin, H. 1970. Structural basis of peripheral frequency analysis. In *Frequency Analysis and Periodicity Detection in Hearing*. R. Plomp and G. F. Smoorenburg, eds. A. W. Suithoff, Leiden.

Stevens, S. S. 1972. A neural quantum in sensory discrimination. *Science* **177**:749.

Stevens, S. S., J. Volkmann, and E. B. Newman. 1937. A scale for the measurement of psychological magnitude pitch. *J. Acoust. Soc. Am.* **8**:185.

von Békésy, G. 1960. *Experiments in Hearing*. McGraw Hill Book Co., New York.

Whitfield, I. C. 1970. Central nervous processing in relation to spatiotemporal discrimination of auditory patterns. In *Frequency Analysis and Periodicity Detection in Hearing*. R. Plomp and G. F. Smoorenburg, eds. A. W. Suithoff, Leiden.

Zwicker, E., G. Flottorp, and S. S. Stevens. 1957. Critical bandwidth in loudness summation. *J. Acoust. Soc. Am.* **29**:548.

Zwislocki, J. 1965. Analysis of some auditory characteristics. In *Handbook of Mathematical Psychology*. R. D. Luce, R. R. Bush, and E. Galanter, eds. Wiley, New York.

SOUND WAVES, ACOUSTICAL ENERGY, AND THE PERCEPTION OF LOUDNESS

In the preceding chapter we studied simple sound *vibrations* and their subjective effects, without investigating how they actually reach the ear. We referred to experiments in which the sound source (earphone) was placed very close to the eardrum. In this chapter we shall discuss the process of sound energy *propagation* from a distant source to the listener and analyze how this acoustical energy flux determines the sensation of loudness.

3.1 Elastic Waves, Force, Energy, and Power

When sound propagates through a medium, the points of the medium vibrate. If there is no sound at all and if there is no other kind of perturbation, each point of the medium will be at rest and remain so until we do something to the medium. The position in space of a given point of the medium when the latter is totally unperturbed is called the *equilibrium position* of that point.

Sound waves are a particular form of so-called *elastic* waves. Whenever we produce a sudden deformation at a given place of a medium (e.g., when we hit a piano string with the hammer or when we suddenly displace air by starting the motion of the reed in a clarinet), elastic forces will cause the points close to the initial deformation to start moving. These points, in turn, will push or pull through elastic forces onto other neighboring points passing on to them the order to start moving, and so on. This "chain reaction" represents an elastic wave propagating away from the region of the initial perturbation. *What* propagates away with this wave is not matter but *energy:* that energy needed to put in motion each point reached by the wave. Sound waves of interest to music are elastic waves in which the points execute motions that are periodic. In its vibration each point of the medium always remains very, very close to the equilibrium position. A sound wave propagates with a well-defined speed away from the source in a straight line, until it is absorbed or reflected. The way sound waves propagate, are reflected, and absorbed determines the acoustical qualities of a room or concert hall.

We have mentioned above the concepts of force and energy. We must now specify their precise physical meaning. Everybody has an intuitive notion of *force:* the pull or the push we have to apply to change a body's shape, to set an object in motion, to hold a body in our hand, to slow a motion down, etc. But physics is not satisfied with intuitive concepts. We must give a clear definition of force, as well as the "recipe" of how to measure it. Both definition and recipe must be based on certain experiments whose results are condensed or summarized in the formulation of a physical law.

It is our daily experience that in order to change the form of a body we have to do something quite specific to it: we have to "apply a force." Deformation, i.e., a change in shape, is not the only possible effect of a force acting on a body. Indeed, it also is our daily experience that in order to alter the motion of a body we must apply a force. Quite generally it is found that the acceleration a of a body, representing the rate of change of its velocity, caused by a given force F is proportional to the latter. Or, conversely, the force is proportional to the acceleration produced: $F = ma$. This is called Newton's equation. The constant of proportionality m is the *mass* of the body. It represents its "inertia" or "resistance" to a change of motion. If more than one force is acting on a body, the resulting acceleration will be given by the *sum* of all forces. This sum may be zero; in that case the acting forces are in *equilibrium.*

The unit of force is defined as that force needed to accelerate a body of 1 kilogram at a rate of 1 m/sec². This unit of force is called the *Newton.* One Newton turns out to be equal to 0.225 pounds force. The pound is a unit of force (weight) most familiar to the public in English-speaking countries. Since the acceleration of gravity is 9.8 m/sec², the weight of a body of 1 kg mass turns out to be 9.8 Newton (= 2.2 lbs.). We can measure a force by measuring the acceleration it imparts to a body of given mass or by equilibrating it (i.e., canceling its effect) with a known force, for instance, the tension in a calibrated spring.[1]

In many physical situations, a given force is applied or "spread" over an extended surface of the body. For instance, in a high-flying aircraft with a pressurized cabin, the air inside exerts a considerable outward-directed force, F, on each window (and on any other part of the hull), that is proportional to the surface of the window, S. The

---

[1] "Calibrated" means that we have previously determined how much the spring stretches for a given force, e.g., a given weight.

relation $p = F/S$ represents the *air pressure* inside the cabin. In general, we define the air pressure as the ratio between the force acting on a surface S that separates the air from vacuum. If instead of vacuum we merely have a different pressure p' on the other side of the surface, the force F acting on S will be given by

$$F = (p - p')S \qquad (3.1)$$

All this is very important for music. Sound waves in air are *air pressure oscillations*. Thus, if in relation (3.1) S corresponds to the surface of the eardrum, p' is the (constant) pressure in the middle ear, and p the oscillating pressure in the meatus (Fig. 2.6), F will be the oscillating force acting on the eardrum, responsible for its motion and that of the bone chain in the middle ear.

The pressure is expressed in Newtons per square meter. The normal atmospheric pressure at sea level is about *100,000 Newton/m²*. A more familiar unit is pound per square inch (for instance, the overpressure in auto tires is usually quoted in these units). Converting Newtons into lbs and m² into sq in, we obtain 1 Newton/m² = 0.00015 lbs/sq in. Normal air pressure at sea level is thus about 15 lbs/sq in.

We now turn to the concept of *energy*. Again, we do have some intuitive idea about it—but our intuition may easily fool us in this case. For instance, some people are tempted to say that "it requires a lot of energy to hold a heavy bag for a long time"—yet for the physicist no energy is involved (except during the act of lifting the bag or putting it down). For the physiologist, on the other hand, a continuous flow of chemical energy to the muscles is necessary, to maintain a continued state of contraction of the muscular fibers. To avoid confusion, it is necessary to introduce the concept of energy in a more precise, quantitative way.

The concept of force alone does not suffice for the solution of practical problems in physics. For instance, we need to know for how long, or over what distance, a given force has been acting, if we want to determine, say, the final speed acquired by a body accelerated by that force (even the largest force may have only a small *end* effect, if the duration or the path of its action was very short). As a matter of fact, what really counts to determine a given change of speed, say from a value 0 to v, is the product of *force times distance traveled* in the direction of the force. If we call x that distance, it can be shown mathematically, based on Newton's equation, that $F \cdot x = \frac{1}{2}mv^2$. The product $F \cdot x$ is called *work* and is counted positive if the displacement x is in the same direction as the force F. The product $\frac{1}{2}mv^2$ is called the *kinetic energy* of the body of mass m. If $F \cdot x$ is positive we interpret the above relation by saying that the work of the force has increased the kinetic energy of the body, or, equivalently, that "work has been delivered to the system," increasing its kinetic energy from zero to $\frac{1}{2}mv^2$.

Work and kinetic energy are measured in Newton times meter. This unit is called *Joule*, after a British physicist and engineer. A body of 1 kg (unit of mass), moving at a speed of 1 m/sec thus has a kinetic energy of 0.5 Joule. If it moves with twice that velocity, its kinetic energy will be four times larger: 2 Joules. An average person (70 kg), running at a speed of 3 m/sec (6.75 miles/h) has a kinetic energy of 315 Joules; that of a 2,000 kg car cruising at 30 m/sec (67.5 miles/h) is 900,000 Joules.

Energy can appear in forms other than kinetic. Consider a body attached to a spring. We have to supply a given amount of work in order to compress the spring. If we do this very, very slowly, practically no kinetic energy will be involved. Rather, the supplied work will be converted into *potential energy;* in this case *elastic* potential energy of the body attached to a compressed spring. Releasing the spring, the body will be accelerated by the force of the expanding spring and the potential energy will be converted into kinetic energy. We may say that potential energy is the *energy of position* of a body, kinetic energy its *energy of motion.*

The sum of potential and kinetic energy of a body is called its total *mechanical energy* (there are many other forms of energy which we will not consider: thermal, chemical, electromagnetic, etc.). There are important cases in which the mechanical energy of a body remains constant. A "musically" important case is the previous example of a body attached to a spring oscillating back and forth under the action of the elastic force of the spring. It can be shown that the resulting vibration about the equilibrium position is *harmonic* (provided the amplitude remains small). When the body is released from a stretched position, its initial kinetic energy is zero. But it possesses an initial elastic potential energy which, as the oscillation starts, is converted into kinetic energy. Whenever the body is passing through its equilibrium position, the elastic potential energy is instantaneously zero while its kinetic energy is maximum. During the harmonic oscillation there is a back-and-forth conversion of potential energy into kinetic, and vice-versa.

The total mechanical energy remains constant as long as no "dissipative" forces are in action. Friction causes a continuous decrease of total energy and hence a decrease of the amplitude of oscillation. The resulting motion is called a *damped oscillation.* It is extremely important in music. Indeed, many musical instruments involve damped oscillations; a vibrating piano string is a typical example. Other external forces may act in such a way as to gradually increase the mechanical energy. They can be used to compensate dissipative losses and thus maintain an oscillation at constant amplitude. A bowed violin string is a typical example: the forces that appear in the bowing mechanism feed energy into the vibrating string at a rate that is equal to the rate of energy loss through friction and acoustical radiation (Section 4.2).

Now we come to a last, but utmost important point concerning energy. Machines (and humans) deliver energy *at a given rate*. Any machine (or human) can perform an almost arbitrarily large amount of work—but it would take a very long time to do so! What really defines the "quality" or "power" of a machine is the *rate* at which it can deliver energy (i.e., perform work). This rate, if constant, is given by

$$P = \frac{\text{work done}}{\text{time employed}} = \frac{W}{(t_2 - t_1)} \tag{3.2}$$

W is the work delivered between the times t_1 and t_2. P is called mechanical *power*. It is measured in units of Joule/sec, called *Watt* (another British engineer). If you are walking up a staircase, your body is delivering a power of about 600 Watt; the electrical energy consumed per second by an electric iron is about 1,000 Watt, and the maximum power delivered by a small car engine is 30 kilowatt (1 horsepower = 0.735 kW). A trombone playing fortissimo emits a total acoustical energy of about 6 Watt.

The concept of power is most important for physics of music. Indeed, our ear is not interested at all in the total acoustical energy which reaches the eardrum—rather, it is sensitive to the *rate* at which this energy arrives, i.e., the acoustical *power*. This rate is what determines the sensation of *loudness*.

3.2 Propagation Speed, Wavelength, and Acoustical Power

After the excursion into the field of "pure" physics in the preceding section, we are in a better condition to understand the phenomenon of wave propagation. To that effect we make use of a *model* of the medium. We imagine the latter as made up of small bodies of given mass, linked to each other with compressed springs (representing the elastic forces). Initially, the spring forces are in equilibrium and all points are at rest. Fig. 3.1 shows the situation when point P has been suddenly displaced an amount x_1 to the right.

Considering the forces shown in Fig. 3.1 we realize that both points Q and R—which initially are at rest at their respective equilibrium

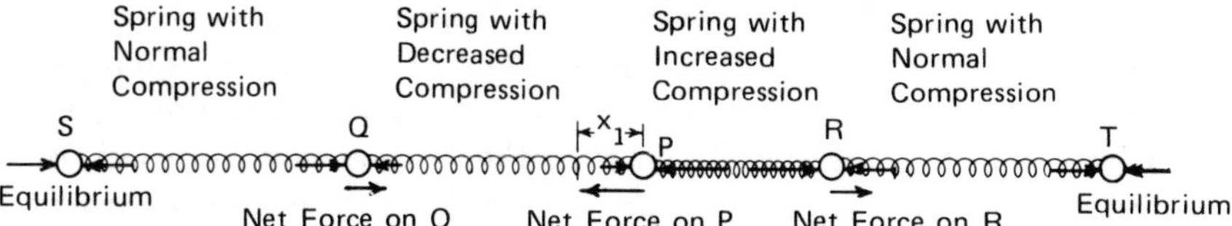

Fig. 3.1. One-dimensional model of an elastic medium (springs in compression), in which point P has been displaced longitudinally.

positions—are subject to a *resultant* force acting toward the right. In other words, according to Newton's equation they will be accelerated to the right and start a motion into the same direction in which P had originally been displaced. This point P, on the other hand, will be on its way back to its equilibrium position, accelerated by a resultant force that acts on it toward the left (Fig. 3.1). A short time later, when points Q and R are on their way toward the right, the compression of the spring between R and T starts increasing, whereas that of the spring between Q and S decreases. It is easy to see that both points S and T will start being subjected to a net force directed to the right that will cause them to start moving to the right, while Q and R may be on their way back to the left. This process goes on and on, from point to point—representing a wave propagating away from P toward both sides. The wave "front" is nothing but an "order" that goes from point to point telling it: "start moving to your right." The "order" is given by the compressed springs (their elastic forces). At no time is there any net transport of matter involved. We call this case a *longitudinal wave*, because the displacements of the points are directed parallel to the direction of propagation of the wave. In the real case of a sound wave propagating through air, the concerted action of the spring forces acting on points P, Q, R, ... roughly corresponds to the air pressure; variations of these forces (e.g., variations of the distances between points) correspond to the *air pressure variations* of the sound wave.

The one-dimensional model of Fig. 3.1 also shows how energy transport is involved in an elastic wave. In first place, we have to provide work from "outside" to produce the initial displacement x_1 of point P because we have to modify the lengths of the two springs PQ, PR. In other words, we need an energy source. In this case the initial energy is converted into the form of potential (positional) energy of point P. Then, as time goes on, points to the right and to the left of P start moving, and the lengths of their springs change. All these processes involve energy, both kinetic (motion of the points) and potential (compression or expansion of springs). The energy initially given to P is transferred from point to point of the medium, as the wave propagates: we have a *flow* or transport of energy away from the source.

Let us now turn to the case in which the springs in the model are in tension (expanded) instead of being compressed, with neighboring points *pulling* on each other. Physically, this corresponds to a tense violin string. For longitudinal displacements (in the direction along the springs) we obtain a qualitatively similar picture for wave propagation as before, only that all forces shown in Fig. 3.1 are now reversed. But in addition we have an entirely new possibility that does not exist for the case of compressed springs: we may displace point P *perpendicularly* to the x direction (Fig. 3.2) and obtain a different type of wave. Since all spring forces now pull on the points, according to Fig. 3.2, the re-

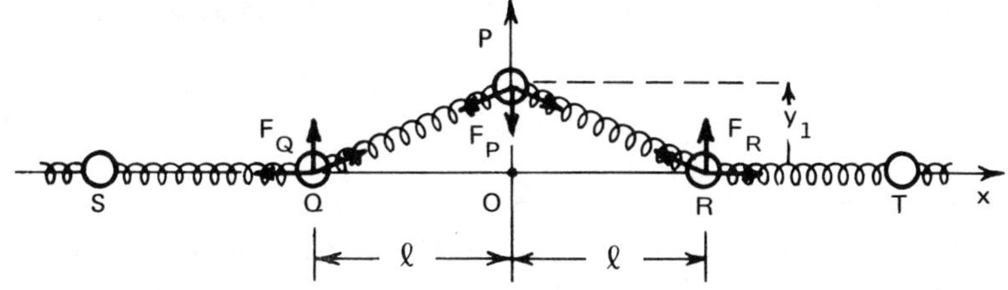

Fig. 3.2. One-dimensional model of an elastic medium (springs in expansion), in which point P has been displaced transversally.

sultant force F_P will accelerate P down to its equilibrium position O. Points Q and R in turn would be subject to net forces that would accelerate them upward, in a direction essentially perpendicular to x. This represents a *transverse* elastic wave, propagating to the right and to the left of P. In a transverse wave, the displacements of the points are perpendicular to the direction of propagation. In a medium under tension, like a violin string, *two* modes of elastic wave propagation may occur simultaneously: transverse and longitudinal.

We now turn to the expression for the speed of propagation of transverse waves. It can be shown by applying Newton's law to the individual points of the unidimensional model of Fig. 3.2 that, for a string under a tension T (in Newton), the velocity V_T of transverse elastic waves is given by:

$$V_T = \sqrt{\frac{T}{d}} \qquad \text{(m/sec)} \qquad (3.3)$$

d is the "linear density" of the medium, i.e., *mass per unit length* (in kg/m). Notice that the more tense a string is, the faster the transverse waves will travel. On the other hand, the more dense it is, the slower the waves will propagate.

A physically equivalent relation exists for the propagation speed of longitudinal waves in a medium of density δ (in kg/m³) and where the pressure is p (in Newton/m²):

$$V_L = \sqrt{\frac{p}{\delta}} \qquad \text{(m/sec)} \qquad (3.4)$$

For an ideal gas, however, the ratio p/δ turns out to be proportional to the "absolute" temperature t_A, defined in terms of the centigrade or Fahrenheit temperatures t_C and t_F by the simple transformation:

$$t_A = 273 + t_C = 273 + \tfrac{5}{9}(t_F - 32) \qquad \text{(degrees)} \qquad (3.5)$$

Notice that at the freezing point ($t_C = 0°C$, $t_F = 32°F$), the absolute temperature is $t_A = 273°$. Although ordinary air is not a 100% "ideal gas," it behaves approximately so, and the velocity of sound waves may be expressed as

$$V_L = 20.1 \sqrt{t_A} \qquad \text{(m/sec)} \qquad (3.6)$$

This turns out to be 331.5 m/sec ($=1087$ feet/sec) at 0°C (32°F) and 334 m/sec ($= 1130$ feet/sec) at 21°C (70°F). The numerical factor in (3.6) is for air only. In general, its value depends on the *composition* of the medium through which the sound propagates. For pure hydrogen, for instance, it is equal to 74.0. Sound waves thus travel almost four times as fast in hydrogen as in air. This leads to funny acoustical effects if a person speaks or sings after having inhaled hydrogen (NO SMOKING!)

Sound travels fast, but not infinitely fast. This, for instance, leads to small but noticeable *arrival time differences* between sound waves from different instruments in a large orchestra and may cause serious problems of rhythmic synchronization. A pianist who for the first time plays on a very large organ, in which the console is far away from the pipes, initially may become quite confused by the late arrival of the sound, out of synchronism with his fingers. *Reverberation* in a hall is based on superposition of delayed sound waves that have suffered multiple reflections on the walls (Section 4.7).

Let us now consider a very long string in which the initial point is set in vibration with simple harmonic motion and continues to vibrate indefinitely compelled by some external force. After a while, all points of the string are found to vibrate with the same simple harmonic motion. If at a given instant of time the initial point is, say, at its maximum displacement, its neighbors are not yet quite there, or just had been there, and so on. Fig. 3.3 shows the transverse displacements of all

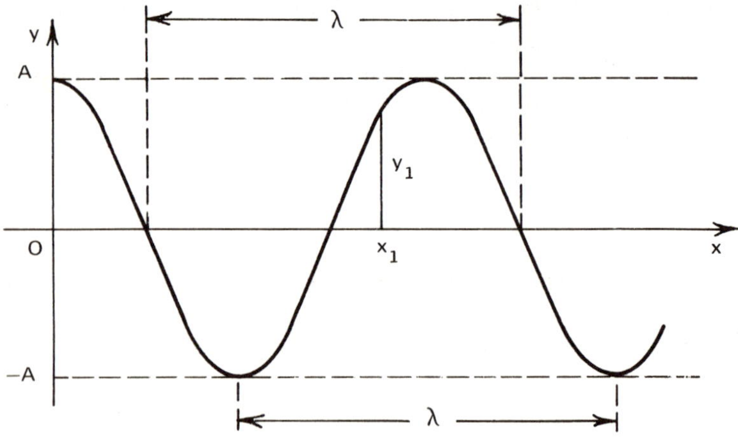

Fig. 3.3

points of the string *at a given time*. This curve is a "snapshot" of the shape of the string during the passage of a sinusoidal transverse wave. The graph in Fig. 3.3 should not be confused with the curve shown in Fig. 2.4, which represents *the time history of only one given point*. The latter indicates a vibration pattern in time, the former a wave pattern in space. The shortest distance between any two points of the string that are vibrating in a parallel way (vibrating "in phase," i.e., having identical displacements y at any given time), is called *wavelength*. It is usually designated with the Greek letter λ. Alternatively the wavelength can be defined as the minimum space interval after which the spatial wave pattern repeats. Compare this with the definition of the period, which represents the minimum *time* interval after which the vibration pattern of *one given point* repeats (Fig. 2.3b).

As time goes on, the snapshot curve seems to move with the speed of the wave to the right (Fig. 3.4)—yet each point of the string only

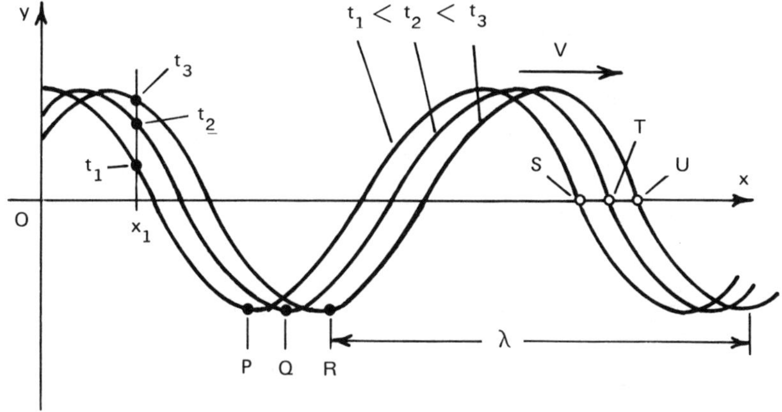

Fig. 3.4

moves up and down (for instance, consider point x_1 in Fig. 3.4). *What moves to the right is the configuration*, i.e., the actual shape of the string, but not the string itself. In other words, what moves to the right is a quality, for instance, the quality of "being at the maximum displacement" (e.g., points P, Q, R in Fig. 3.4), or the quality of "just passing through equilibrium" (points S, T, U). And, of course, what also moves to the right is *energy*, the potential and kinetic energy involved in the up-and-down oscillation of the points of the string.

There is an important relationship between the speed V of a sinusoidal wave, its wavelength λ, and the frequency f of oscillation of the individual points. Considering Fig. 3.3 we realize that the wave will have moved exactly one wavelength λ during the time it takes the initial point (or any other) to make one complete oscillation, i.e., during one period τ. We therefore can write for the speed of the wave:

$$V = \frac{\text{distance traveled}}{\text{time employed}} = \frac{\lambda}{\tau}$$

Since the inverse of the period is equal to the frequency f [relation (2.1)], we can also write

$$V = \lambda \cdot f \tag{3.7}$$

This relation provides the quantitative link between the "space representation" of Fig. 3.3 and the "time representation" of Fig. 2.4. Relation (3.7) enables us to express the wavelength of a transverse wave in a string in terms of the frequency of the oscillation of the individual points and the propagation velocity (3.3):

$$\lambda = \frac{1}{f}\sqrt{\frac{T}{d}} \tag{3.8}$$

In the case of *longitudinal waves* such as a sound wave the points vibrate in a direction *parallel* to the direction of propagation, and it is not so easy to picture their real position in visual form. For this reason, sound waves are more conveniently represented as pressure oscillations. Fig. 3.5 (bottom row) shows the displacements of the points

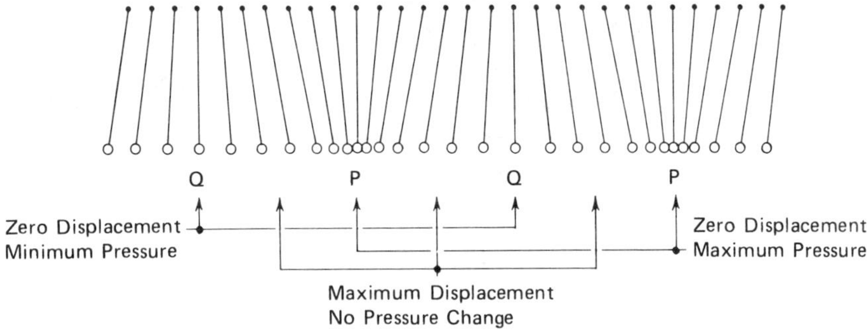

Fig. 3.5. Longitudinal wave in a one-dimensional medium. To show the actual displacements, each point is depicted as the bob of a pendulum.

of a unidimensional model of the medium, when a longitudinal wave is passing through. Notice that points show their maximum accumulation (i.e., maximum pressure) and maximum rarefaction (i.e., minimum pressure) at the places where their displacement is zero (points P, Q, respectively). On the other hand, at places where the displacements are maximum, the pressure variations are zero. This means that the pressure variations of a sound wave are 90° out of phase with the oscillation of the points: the maximum pressure variations (either increase or decrease) occur at places where the displacements of the points are zero;

conversely, maximum displacements of the points occur at places where the pressure variations are zero.

A sinusoidal sound wave is one in which the pressure at each point oscillates harmonically about the "normal" (undisturbed) value (Fig. 3.6):

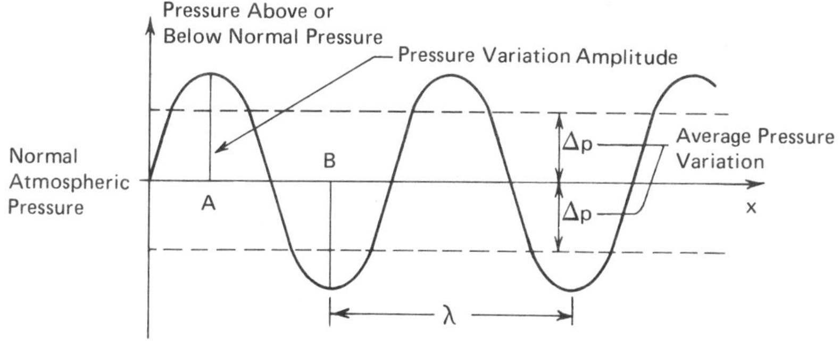

Fig. 3.6

At a point like A, all points of the medium have come closest to each other (maximum pressure increase, points P in Fig. 3.5); at a point like B, they have moved away from each other (maximum pressure decrease, points Q in Fig. 3.5). The *average pressure variation*, Δp, is equal to the pressure variation amplitude divided by $\sqrt{2}$ ($= 1.41$). Taking into account relations (3.6) and (3.7) we obtain for the wavelength of sinusoidal sound waves in air:

$$\lambda = \frac{20.1}{f} \sqrt{t_A} \qquad \text{(in m)} \tag{3.9}$$

t_A is the "absolute" temperature given by (3.5). Typical values of wavelengths at normal temperature are shown in Fig. 3.7.

Elastic waves can be transmitted from one medium to another—for instance, from air into water, from air into a wall and then again into air, from a string to a wooden plate, and from there to the surrounding air. The nature of the wave may change in each transition (e.g., the transition from a transverse wave in the string and plate to a longitudinal sound wave in the air). However, in each transition, *the frequency remains invariant*. The wavelength, on the other hand, will change according to relation (3.7): $\lambda = V/f$. In this relation, V changes from medium to medium, while f is dictated exclusively by the initial vibration (source).

When an elastic wave hits the boundary between two media, part of it is *reflected* back to the original medium. Some boundaries are almost perfect reflectors (e.g., smooth cement walls, for sound waves; the fixed end points of a tense string for transverse waves). This phenomenon is governed by the fact that on the reflecting boundary the

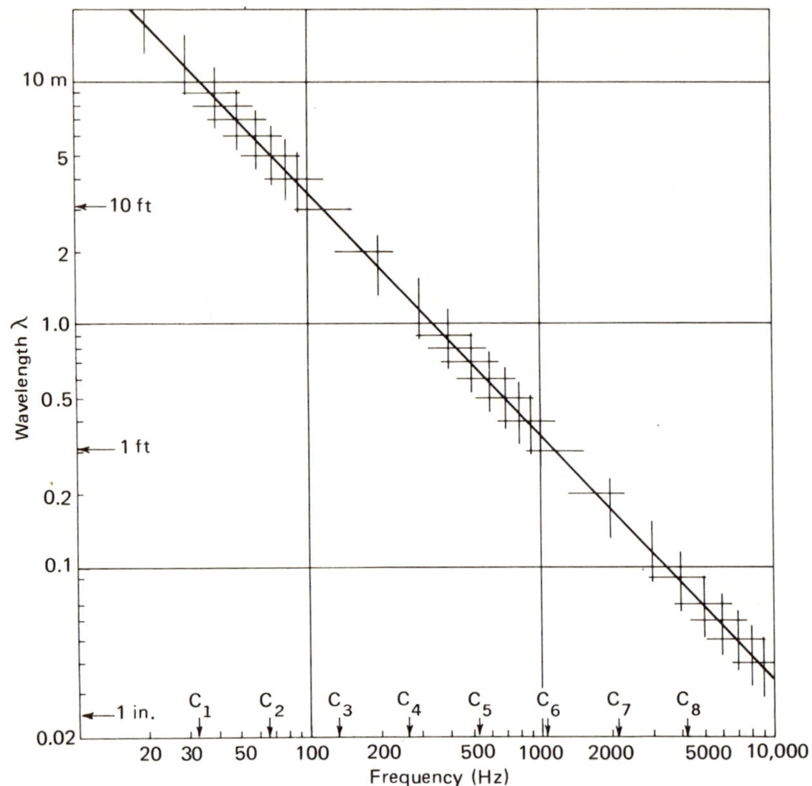

Fig. 3.7. Wavelength of a sound wave in air at normal temperature, as a function of frequency (logarithmic scale).

points of the medium are compelled to remain at rest, therefore upsetting the balance of elastic forces that "command" the wave propagation. In a reflection, the frequency remains unchanged, while the direction of propagation is reversed for a perpendicular incidence (or, in general, directed with a reflection angle equal to the incidence angle). Also the amplitude would remain the same if there were no absorption.

We finally consider the *energy flow* associated with a sound wave. We define it as the amount of total mechanical energy (potential and kinetic, associated with the elastic oscillations of the points of the medium) that is transferred during each second through a surface of unit area ($1\ \mathrm{m^2}$) perpendicular to the direction of propagation (Fig. 3.8). This energy flow is expressed in Joule per $\mathrm{m^2}$ and sec, or, taking into account the definition and the units of power (3.2), in Watt/$\mathrm{m^2}$. It is more commonly called the *intensity* of the wave, and designated with the letter I. It can be shown that there is a relation between the intensity of a sinusoidal sound wave and the value of the *average pressure oscillation* associated with the wave (see Fig. 3.6), which we denote with

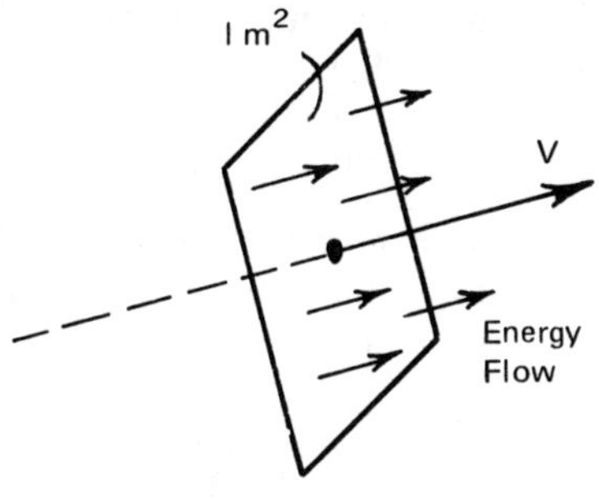

Fig. 3.8

Δp (equal to the pressure variation amplitude divided by $\sqrt{2}$):

$$I = \frac{(\Delta p)^2}{V \delta}$$

In this relation, V is the speed of the sound wave (3.6) and δ is the air density. For normal conditions of temperature and pressure, we have the following numerical relationship:

$$I = 0.00234 \times (\Delta p)^2 \qquad (\text{Watt/m}^2) \tag{3.10}$$

Δp must be expressed in Newton/m². As we shall see in Section 3.4, the faintest pure sound that can be heard at a frequency of 1,000 Hz has an intensity of only 10^{-12} Watt/m². According to relation (3.10) this represents an average pressure variation of only 2.0×10^{-5} Newton/m², i.e., only 2.0×10^{-10} that of the normal atmospheric pressure! This gives an idea of how sensitive the ear is.

A given sound source (a musical instrument or a loudspeaker) emits sound waves into all directions. In general, the amount of energy emitted per second depends on the particular direction considered. Let I_1 be the intensity of the wave at point A_1 propagating along the direction shown in Fig. 3.9. This means that an amount of energy $I_1 a_1$ flows through the surface a_1 during each second. If we assume that no energy

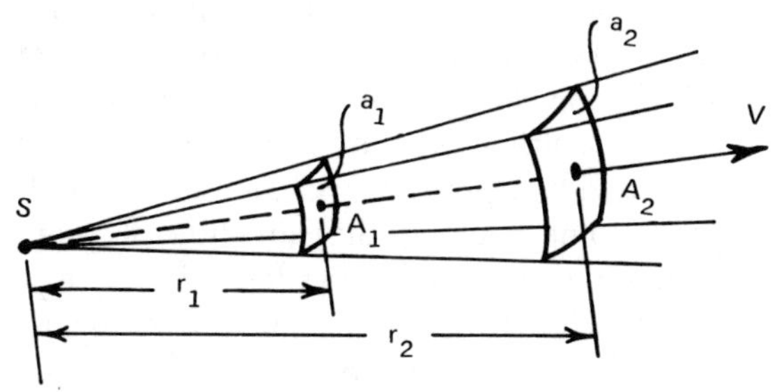

Fig. 3.9

is lost on its way, this same amount of energy will flow each second through surface a_2 at point A_2. Therefore

$$I_1 a_1 = I_2 a_2$$

Since the areas of the surfaces a_1 and a_2 are proportional to the squares of their respective distances r_1 and r_2 to the source, the intensity of a sound wave varies inversely proportional to the square of the distance to the source:

$$\frac{I_1}{I_2} = \left(\frac{r_2}{r_1}\right)^2 \tag{3.11}$$

This law is no longer true if we take into account sound reflections and absorption.

If we imagine the whole sound source encircled by a spherical surface, the total amount of energy flowing each second through that surface is called the *power output* of the source. It represents the rate at which the source emits energy into *all* directions in form of sound waves. Its value is given in Watts (Joule/sec). Typical instruments radiate between 0.01 Watt (clarinet) up to 6.4 Watts (trombone playing fortissimo). A good hi-fi speaker can emit up to 150 Watts in form of sound waves.

3.3 Superposition of Waves; Standing Waves

In absence of reflecting walls, sound waves travel in straight lines away from the source. As shown in the previous section, their intensity decreases rapidly, proportional to $1/r^2$, where r is the distance to the source. If we have more than one source, the waves emitted by each one will propagate individually as if no other wave would exist, and the resultant effect at one given point of the medium (for instance in the auditory canal) will be a pressure oscillation that is simply given by the algebraic sum of the pressure oscillations of the individual waves.[2] In other words, *sound waves superpose linearly*.

Let us consider the superposition of two pure sound waves of frequencies f_1 and f_2 and, according to relation (3.7), of wavelengths $\lambda_1 = V/f_1$, $\lambda_2 = V/f_2$, traveling in the *same* direction. In order to obtain a "snapshot" of the resulting pressure variations, we just have to add the values of the individual pressure variations, as caused by each wave separately at each point x along the direction of propagation. Since the velocity of sound waves does not depend on frequency (nor on the vibration pattern as a whole), all points of the medium will repeat exactly the same complex vibration pattern—only subject to a different timing. The energy flow—i.e., the intensity of the superposition of two

---

[2] Note carefully that what is added here are pressure *variations*, and not absolute values of the pressure!

(or more) waves traveling in the same direction with the *same phase*—is simply the sum of the energy flow contributions from the individual components:

$$I = I_1 + I_2 + I_3 + \cdots \qquad (3.12)$$

A particularly important case is that of two sinusoidal waves of the same frequency and the same amplitude *traveling in opposite directions*. This, for instance, happens when a sinusoidal wave is reflected at a given point (without absorption) and then travels back, superposing itself with the incoming wave. Let us first consider transverse waves in a string (Fig. 3.10). Adding the contributions from each component,

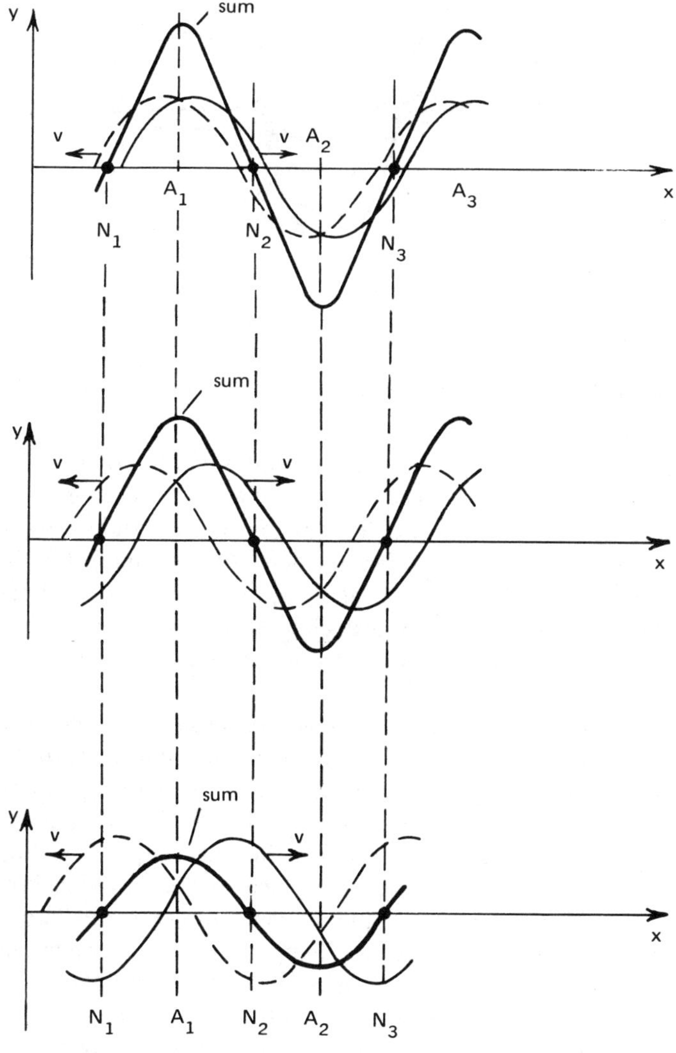

Fig. 3.10

we obtain another sinusoidal wave of the same frequency but of different amplitude. The striking fact, however, is that this resultant wave *does not propagate at all!* It remains anchored at certain points N_1, N_2, N_3 . . . . called *nodes,* which do not vibrate. Points between nodes vibrate with different amplitudes, depending on their position. In particular, points A_1, A_2, A_3 . . . . . (midway between nodes), called *antinodes,* vibrate with a maximum amplitude (twice that of each component wave). Fig. 3.11 shows the successive shapes of a string when

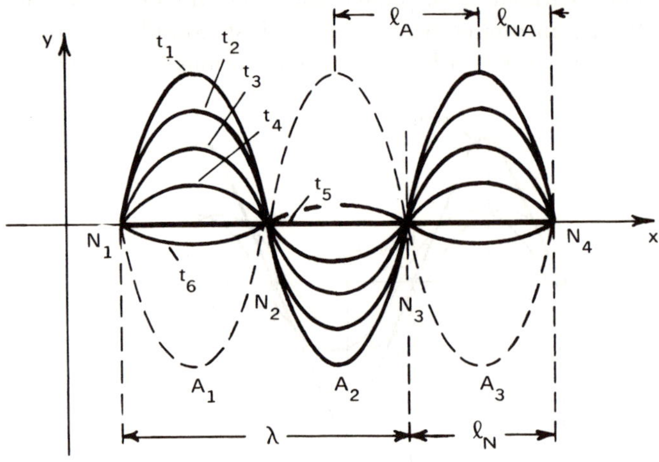

Fig. 3.11. Successive shapes of a string in a standing wave oscillation.

two sinusoidal waves of the same amplitude travel in opposite directions. This is called a *standing wave.* Points oscillate, but there is no evidence of propagation. The wave profile changes in amplitude, but does not move neither to the right nor to the left. At one time (t_1) the string shows a maximum deformation; at another (t_5) it has no deformation at all. As we shall see in the next chapter, standing waves play a key role in music, especially in the sound generation mechanisms of musical instruments.

In a standing wave *there is no net propagation of energy,* either. The whole string almost acts as one elastic vibrating spring: at one given time (e.g., t_5 in Fig. 3.11), all points are passing through their equilibrium position, and the energy of the whole string is in kinetic form (energy of motion). At another instant (e.g., t_1 in Fig. 3.11), all points are at their maximum displacement and the energy is all potential. In other words, in a standing wave all points oscillate in phase. Note carefully that this does not happen with a propagating wave: in Fig. 3.3, for instance, at one given instant of time there are points which have maximum displacement (only potential energy) as well as points with zero displacement (only kinetic energy), or points in any intermediate situation (both forms of energy). Furthermore, in a propagating wave all points have the same amplitude; what varies are the times at which a maximum displacement is attained (the points are out of phase).

A careful inspection of Fig. 3.11 reveals that the distance l_N between two neighboring nodes N_1, N_2, or the distance l_A between two antinodes A_1, A_2 is exactly one half of a wavelength λ:

$$l_N = l_A = \frac{\lambda}{2} \tag{3.13}$$

On the other hand, the distance l_{NA} between a node N_1 and an antinode A_1 is a quarter wavelength:

$$l_{NA} = \frac{\lambda}{4} \tag{3.14}$$

Standing waves can also be longitudinal. They arise when two sound waves of the same frequency and pressure variation amplitude travel in opposite directions. This happens, for instance, when a sound wave travels along a pipe and is reflected at the other end; standing waves also arise from reflections on the walls in rooms and halls. They have the same properties as transverse standing waves, and the discussion given above applies here, too. There is, however, an important additional remark to be made. As pointed out in the previous section, sound waves are most conveniently described by pressure oscillations. We showed there that points with maximum pressure variation have zero longitudinal displacement (Fig. 3.5), whereas places with zero pressure variation correspond to points with maximum displacement. We can translate this to the case of a standing sound wave: *pressure nodes* (i.e., points whose pressure variations are permanently zero) *are vibration antinodes* (points which oscillate with maximum amplitude), whereas *pressure antinodes* (points at which the pressure oscillates with maximum amplitude) *are vibration nodes* (points which remain permanently at rest).

3.4 Intensity, Sound Level, and Loudness

In Section 2.3 we stated that, for a pure sound, the amplitude of the eardrum oscillations leads to the sensation of loudness. This amplitude is directly related to the average pressure variation, Δp, of the incoming sound wave and, hence, to the acoustical energy flow or intensity I reaching the ear (relation 3.10). We start here by investigating the range of intensities I of pure sound waves to which the ear is sensitive. There are two limits of sensitivity to a tone of given frequency: (1) a lower limit or *threshold of hearing* representing the minimum just audible intensity; (2) an *upper limit of hearing* beyond which physiological pain is evoked, eventually leading to physical damage of the hearing mechanism. One finds that these two limits vary from individual to individual and depend on the particular frequency under consideration. In general, for a tone of about 1,000 Hz (a pitch between the notes B_5 and C_6), the interval between limits is largest. The enormous range of intensities encompassed between the two limits of hearing is startling. Indeed, for a tone of 1,000 Hz, it is found that the average threshold intensity lies near 10^{-12} Watt/m², whereas the limit of pain lies at about 1 Watt/m². This represents a ratio of intensities of one trillion to one, to which the ear is sensitive! Table 3.1 shows the relations between sound intensity and musical loudness sensation, for a 1,000 Hz tone:

Table 3.1

Intensity (Watt/m²)	*Loudness*
1	limit of pain
10^{-3}	*fff*
10^{-4}	*ff*
10^{-5}	*f*
10^{-6}	*mf*
10^{-7}	*p*
10^{-8}	*pp*
10^{-9}	*ppp*
10^{-12}	threshold of hearing

At 1,000 Hz, the intensity range of *musical* interest extends from about 10^{-9} to 10^{-2} Watt/m². This still represents a variation of a factor of ten millions!

Because of this tremendous range, the unit of Watt/m² is impractical. There is another reason why it is impractical. The just noticeable difference (jnd) of a given stimulus is usually a good physical "gauge" to take into account when it comes to choose an appropriate unit for the corresponding physical magnitude. Experiments show that the *jnd in tone intensity* is roughly proportional to the intensity of the tone.[3] This proportionality thus suggests that the appropriate "unit" should gradually increase, as the intensity of the tone we want to describe increases. This, of course, would lead to an awful complication unless we introduce a different magnitude which is an appropriate function of the intensity I. This new magnitude should accomplish three simultaneous objectives: (1) a "compression" of the whole audible intensity scale into a much

---

[3] Like the jnd in frequency, the jnd in intensity has a "fine structure" related to the "neural quantum" of loudness detection (Stevens 1972) (see also Section 2.3).

smaller range of values; (2) the use of relative values (for instance, relative to the threshold of hearing) rather than absolute ones; and (3) the introduction of a more convenient unit whose value closely represents the minimum perceptible change of sound intensity.

The introduction of the new quantity is done in the following way. Note in Table 3.1 that what seems more characteristically related to the loudness effect is the *exponent* to which the number 10 is raised when we quote the value of the sound intensity (left column): -12 for the threshold of hearing, -9 for a *ppp* sound, -7 for piano, -5 for forte, -3 for forte-fortissimo, and 0 for limit of pain ($10^0 = 1$). This strongly suggests that we should use what in mathematics is called a logarithmic function to represent intensity.

The *decimal logarithm* of a given number is the exponent to which 10 has to be raised in order to yield that number. For instance, the logarithm of 100 is 2 because $10^2 = 100$; the logarithm of 10,000 is 4 because $10^4 = 10,000$; the logarithm of 1 is zero, because $10^0 = 1$; and the logarithm of 0.000001 is -6 because $10^{-6} = 0.000001$. These relations are written symbolically: $\log 100 = 2$; $\log 10,000 = 4$; $\log 1 = 0$; $\log 0.000001 = -6$. For any number intermediate between integer powers of ten, the logarithm can be found through the use of tables.

An important property is that the logarithm of the *product* of two numbers is the *sum* of the logarithms of the individual numbers. For instance, the logarithm of the number 10^4 *times* 10^3 is 4 *plus* 3 (i.e., 7), because $10^4 \times 10^3 = 10^{4+3} = 10^7$. In general, for any two numbers a and b, we have the relation $\log (a \times b) = \log a + \log b$. For the logarithm of a division a/b, we have, instead, $\log (a/b) = \log a - \log b$.

Decimal logarithms can be used to define a more appropriate magnitude to describe sound intensity. First of all, we adopt the hearing threshold (at 1,000 Hz) of 10^{-12} Watt/m² as our *reference* intensity I_0. Then we introduce the quantity

$$SL = 10 \times \log \frac{I}{I_0} \tag{3.15}$$

This is called the sound intensity level. The unit of SL is called the *decibel,* denoted "db." For the hearing threshold, $I/I_0 = 1$ and $SL = 0$ db. For the upper limit of hearing $I/I_0 = 10^{12}$ and $SL = 10 \times \log 10^{12} = 120$ db. A "forte" sound (Table 3.1) has a sound intensity level of 70 db; *ppp* corresponds to 30 db.

It is important to note that when a quantity is expressed in decibels, a *relative* measure is given, with respect to some reference value (e.g., the hearing threshold in the definition of SL). Whenever the intensity I is multiplied by a factor of ten, one just *adds* ten decibels to the value of SL; when the intensity is multiplied by 100, one must add 20 db, etc. Likewise, when the intensity is divided by a factor of 100, one must *subtract* 20 db from SL. Table 3.2 gives some useful relations.

Table 3.2

Change in SL	What Happens to the Intensity
add (subtract) 1 db	multiply (divide) by 1.26
$+(-)$ 3 db	$\times(\div)$ 2
$+(-)$ 10 db	$\times(\div)$ 10
$+(-)$ 20 db	$\times(\div)$ 100
$+(-)$ 60 db	$\times(\div)$ 1,000,000

We may use relation (3.10) to express the intensity in terms of the much more easily measurable average pressure variation, Δp. We find that the minimum threshold I_0 at 1,000 Hz roughly corresponds to an average pressure variation $\Delta p_0 = 2 \times 10^{-5}$ Newton/m². Since according to relation (3.10) I is proportional to the *square* of Δp, we have

$$\log \frac{I}{I_0} = \log \left(\frac{\Delta p}{\Delta p_0}\right)^2 = 2 \times \log \frac{\Delta p}{\Delta p_0}$$

Hence, one may introduce the quantity

$$SPL = 20 \times \log \frac{\Delta p}{\Delta p_0} \tag{3.16}$$

called the *sound pressure level*. For a traveling wave, the numerical values of (3.15) and (3.16) are identical, and *SL* and *SPL* represent one and the same thing. For *standing* waves, however, there is no energy flow at all (Section 3.3) and the intensity I as used in (3.16) cannot be defined; hence *SL* loses its meaning. Yet the concept of average pressure variation Δp at a given point in space (e.g., at the entrance to the auditory canal) still remains meaningful and so does the sound pressure level. This is why relation (3.16) is more frequently used than (3.15). Note carefully that the definitions of *SL* and *SPL* do not involve at all the frequency of the sound wave. Although we did make reference to a 1,000 Hz tone, nothing prevents us from defining *SL* and *SPL* through relations (3.15) and (3.16), respectively, for any arbitrary frequency. What does depend on frequency, and very strongly, are the subjective limits of hearing (e.g., I_0 and p_0) and, in general, the *subjective* sensation of loudness, as we shall see further below.

Funny things seem to happen with the sound level, or sound pressure level, when we superpose two sounds of the same frequency (and phase). Just consider Table 3.2: adding two tones of the same intensity, which according to (3.12) means doubling the intensity, adds a mere 3 db to the sound level of the original sound, whatever the actual value of that SL might have been. Superposing *ten* equal tones (in phase) only increases by 10 db the resulting *SL*. To raise the *SL* of a given tone by 1 db , we must multiply its intensity by 1.26, meaning that we must add a tone whose intensity is 0.26 (about $\frac{1}{4}$) that of the original tone.

The minimum change in SPL required to give rise to a detectable change in the loudness sensation (jnd in sound level) is roughly constant and of the order of 0.2–0.4 db in the musically relevant range of pitch and loudness. The unit of SL or SPL, the decibel, is thus indeed of "reasonable size"—close to the jnd.

There is an alternative way of looking at the jnd of intensity or sound level. Instead of asking how much the intensity of *one* given tone must be changed to give a just noticeable effect, we may pose the totally equivalent question: what is the minimum intensity I_2 that a *second* tone of the same frequency and phase must have, to be noticed in presence of the first one (whose intensity I_1 is kept constant)? That minimum intensity I_2 is called the *threshold of masking*. The original tone of constant intensity I_1 is called the "masking tone," the additional tone is the "masked tone." Masking plays a key role in music. In this paragraph we only mention the masking of tones of frequency (and phase) identical to that of the masking tone; further below we shall discuss masking at different frequencies. The relation between the masking level ML (SL of the masked tone at threshold) and the jnd of sound level can be found using relation (3.15) and taking into account the properties of logarithms. For instance, for a jnd of 0.2 db one obtains a masking level ML that is 13 db less than the SL of the masking tone; a jnd of 0.4 db corresponds to a ML that is 10 db below.

So far we have been dealing with the physical quantities SL and SPL. Now we must examine the psychophysical magnitude *loudness*, associated with a given SPL. In Sections 1.4 and 2.3 we mentioned the ability of individuals to establish an order for the "strength" of two sensations of the same kind, pointing out that complications arise when absolute quantitative comparisons are to be made. In the case of loudness, judgments of whether two pure tones sound equally loud show fairly low dispersion among different individuals. But judgments on "how much" louder one tone is than another require previous conditioning or training and yield results that fluctuate greatly from individual to individual and from occasion to occasion.

Tones of the same SPL but with different frequency in general are judged as having different loudness. The SPL is thus not a good measure of loudness, if we intercompare tones of different frequency. Experiments have been performed to establish *curves of equal loudness,* taking the SPL at 1,000 Hz as a reference quantity.[4] These are shown in Fig. 3.12 (Fletcher and Munson 1933). Starting from the vertical axis cen-

---

[4] Obtained through "loudness matching" experiments conducted in a way quite similar to pitch matching experiments.

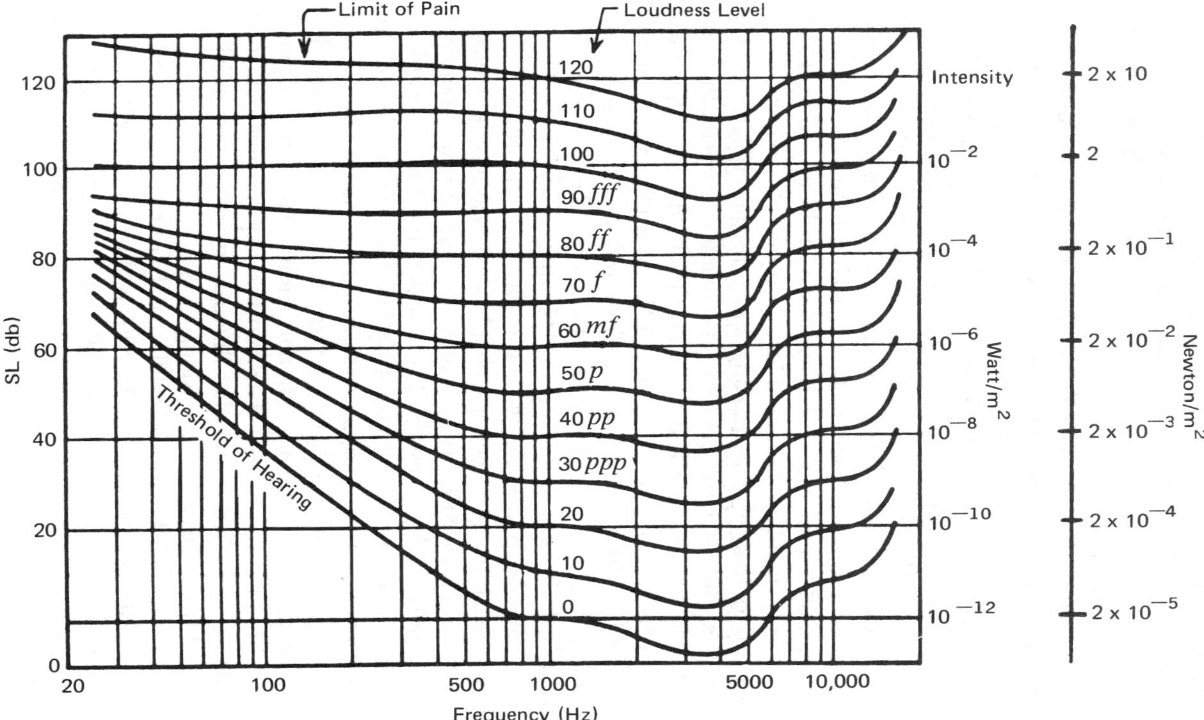

Fig. 3.12. Curves of equal loudness (Fletcher and Munson 1933) in a sound level (*SL*) and frequency diagram. The corresponding scales of sound intensity and average pressure variation are also shown. Reprinted by permission from the *Journal of the Acoustical Society of America.*

tered at 1,000 Hz toward both sides of lower and higher frequencies, respectively, are drawn curves that correspond to *SPL*'s of tones that are judged "equally loud" as the reference tone of 1,000 Hz. Note, for instance, that while a *SPL* of 50 db (intensity of 10^{-7} Watt/m^2) at 1,000 Hz is considered "piano," the same *SPL* is barely audible at 60 Hz. In other words, to produce a given loudness sensation at low frequencies, say a "forte" sound, a much higher intensity (energy flow) is needed than at 1,000 Hz. This is why bass tones seem to "fade away" much before the trebles, when we gradually move away from a fixed sound source. Or why we have to pay so much more for a hi-fi set, particularly the speakers, if we want well-balanced basses.

The lowest curve in Fig. 3.12 represents the threshold of hearing for different frequencies. Again, it shows how the sensitivity of the ear decreases considerably toward low (and also toward very high) frequencies. Maximum sensitivity is achieved at about 3,000 Hz. The shape of this threshold curve is influenced by the acoustical properties of the auditory canal (meatus) and by the mechanical properties of the bone chain in the middle ear. In particular, the high sensitivity around 3,000 Hz is due to the fact that the auditory canal has a resonance and builds up standing waves at that frequency. Finally, it should be emphasized that the curves in Fig. 3.12 are valid only for *single, continuously sounding pure tones*. We shall discuss further below what happens to the loudness sensation if a tone is of short duration (less than a second).

Now comes a sometimes confusing issue. A new quantity is introduced, called the *loudness level*, which we designate *LL*. It is defined in the following way. The *LL* of a tone of frequency *f* is given by the *SPL* of a tone of 1,000 Hz that is judged to be equally loud. This means that the curves of Fig. 3.12 are curves of constant loudness level. The unit of *LL* is called the *phon*. Since for 1,000 Hz *LL* coincides with the *SPL*, 1 phon at 1,000 Hz is equal to 1 db. At other frequencies, however, this identity vanishes. At very low frequencies, the curves in Fig. 3.12 are more crowded together, so that there, 1 phon is considerably *smaller* than 1 db. Fig. 3.12 can be used to find the *LL* of a tone of given *SPL*, at any frequency *f*. For instance, consider a tone of 70 db *SPL* ($I = 10^{-5}$ Watt/m^2) at 80 Hz. We see that the curve that passes through that point intersects the 1,000 Hz line at 50 db. The *LL* of that tone is thus equal to 50 phons. In general, the numbers shown along the 1,000 Hz line represent the *LL* in phon of the corresponding constant loudness curves. Note also that the musical loudness notation (*ppp* to *fff*) specifically refers to the loudness level *LL*.

Note very carefully that *LL* still is a *physical* magnitude, rather than a psychophysical one (in spite of the name). It represents those intensities or *SPL's* that sound equally loud, but it does not pretend to represent loudness in an absolute manner: a tone whose *LL* is twice as large simply does not sound twice as loud! Many studies have been made to determine a subjective scale of loudness. Fig. 3.13 (solid line) is the result (Stevens 1955), relating the "subjective loudness" L with the loudness level LL, in the range of musical interest. The quantity L describing subjective loudness is expressed in units called *sones*. Notice that the relationship is not linear (the loudness scale in Fig. 3.13 is what one calls a logarithmic scale). It is such that increasing LL by 10 phons, the loudness L is merely *doubled*. This, for instance, means that *ten* instruments playing a given note at the same LL are judged to sound only *twice* as loud as one of the instruments playing alone!

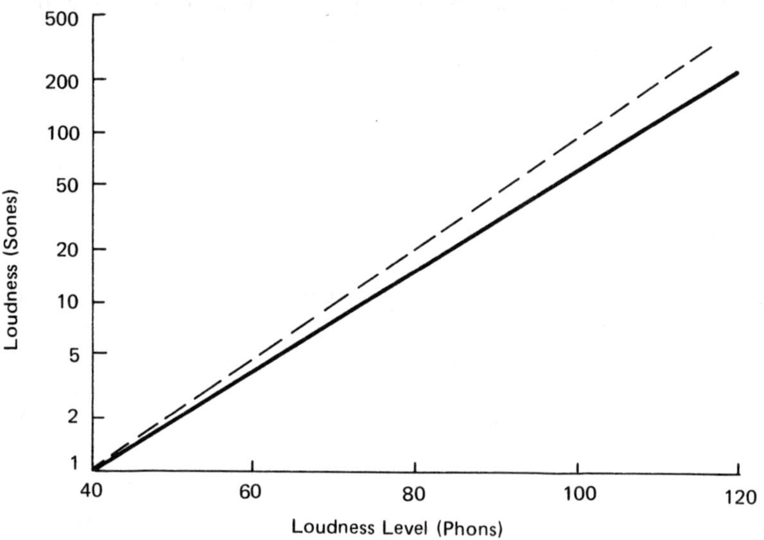

Fig. 3.13. Solid line: experimental relation between the psychological magnitude loudness and the physical magnitude loudness level (after Stevens 1955). Broken line: power-law relationship 3.17 (Stevens 1970).

It has been shown that the relation between L and the wave intensity I, or the average pressure variation Δp, can be described approximately by the simple function (Stevens 1970):

$$L = C_1 \sqrt[3]{I} = C_2 \sqrt[3]{(\Delta p)^2} \tag{3.17}$$

where C_1 and C_2 are parameters that depend on frequency. This yields the broken line shown in Fig. 3.13, which lies well within the statistical fluctuation of the actual measurements (not shown). Notice that the logarithmic relationship [as in (3.15) and (3.16)] is all but gone. Yet an appreciable "compression" of the subjective loudness scale still remains: in order to vary L between 1 and 200, the intensity I must change by a factor of 8 million.

When we superpose two or more tones of the same frequency (and the same phase), the resulting tone has an intensity (energy flow) which is the sum of the intensities of the component tones: $I = I_1 + I_2 + I_3 + \cdots$ (3.12). Since in this case the individual tones cannot be discriminated from each other, this total intensity determines the resulting loudness through relation (3.17). L obviously will not be equal to the sum of the loudnesses of the individual tones. Different situations arise when the component waves have *different frequencies*. We may distinguish three regimes: (1) If the frequencies of the component tones fall all *within the critical band* of the center frequency (Section 2.4), the resulting loudness still is directly related to the total intensity (energy flow), sum of the individual intensities:

$$L = C_1 \sqrt[3]{(I_1 + I_2 + I_3 + \cdots\cdots)} \tag{3.18}$$

This property actually leads to a far more precise determination (Zwicker, Flottorp and Stevens 1957) of the critical band than that given in Section 2.4. (2) When the frequency spread of the multitone stimulus *exceeds the critical band*, the resulting subjective loudness is *greater* than that obtained by simple intensity summation (3.18), tending toward a value that is given by the sum of individual loudnesses:

$$L = C_1 \sqrt[3]{I_1} + C_1 \sqrt[3]{I_2} + C_1 \sqrt[3]{I_3} + \cdots\cdots \tag{3.19}$$

Masking effects must be taken into account if the individual loudnesses L_1, L_2, etc. differ considerably among each other. The limit of loudness integration (3.19) is never achieved in practice. (3) When the frequency difference between individual tones is large, the situation becomes complicated. First of all, difficulties arise with the concept of "total loudness." People tend to focus on only *one* of the component tones (e.g., the loudest, or that of highest pitch) and assign the sensation of total loudness to just that single component:

$$L = \left. \begin{array}{c} \text{maximum} \\ \text{or highest} \end{array} \right\} \text{ of } (L_1, L_2, \ldots) \tag{3.20}$$

This makes loudness matching experiments difficult, if not meaningless.[5]

All this has very important consequences for music. For instance, two organ pipes of the same kind and the same pitch sound only 1.3 times louder than one pipe alone. When their pitch is a semitone or a whole tone apart their loudness still will be roughly 1.3 times that of one single pipe (a semitone or whole tone falls within the critical band, Fig. 2.13). But two tones that are a major third apart will sound

---

[5] A well-known situation, similar to this case, arises with the sensation of pain. If you are pinched in two places very near to each other, the pain is "twice" that of a single pinch (equivalent to case 1 above). But when the places are far apart, you have difficulty in sensing out what one may call "total pain" (case 3). Actually, you will tend to focus on only one of the two stimulations. Quite possibly, the Chinese technique of anesthesia by acupuncture may be based on this effect.

louder than the previous combination. These facts have been well known for centuries to organ builders and composers as well. Since there is no possibility for a manual loudness control of individual organ tones, as in string instruments or woodwinds, loudness on the organ can be altered only by changing the number of simultaneously sounding stops. But since according to the previous paragraph, loudness summation is more effective when the component tones differ in frequency appreciably, stops sounding one (4′ stop), two (2′), or more octaves above [and below (16′)] the written note are mainly used for that purpose.[6] On the other hand, without adding or subtracting stops, loudness may also be controlled through the number of notes simultaneously played. Each new voice entering in a fugue increases the subjective loudness of the piece, and each additional note in a chord accomplishes the same purpose. Some organists play the final chords of a Bach fugue pulling additional stops. This is absurd—Bach himself programmed the desired loudness increase by simply writing in more notes than the number of voices used throughout the fugue!

We have examined the summation of loudness of two or more superposed tones, but we have not yet discussed what happens to the threshold of hearing of a tone when it is sounded in presence of another. If the frequencies of both tones coincide, this threshold is given by the masking level discussed earlier (p. 75). If their frequencies differ, we still can determine a masking level, defined as the minimum sound level which the masked tone must exceed in order to be "singled out" and heard individually in presence of the masking tone. The intensity threshold of isolated pure tones (bottom curve in Fig. 3.12) changes appreciably, that is, increases, if other tones are simultaneously present. The most familiar experience of masking is that of not being able to follow a conversation in presence of a lot of background noise. The masking level ML of a pure tone of frequency f in presence of another pure tone of fixed characteristics (frequency 415 Hz and sound level SL) is shown in Fig. 3.14 (Egan and Hake 1950). The level ML to which the masked tone has to be raised above the normal threshold of hearing (as given by the bottom curve of Fig. 3.12) is represented for different SL values of the masking tone. The regions close to f_0 must be extrapolated to the value deduced from the jnd of loudness (p. 75); beats phenomena play a role there, which have nothing to do with masking per se. At higher SL, additional complications arise due to the appearance of aural harmonics at frequencies $2f_0$, $3f_0$, etc. (Section 2.5). Notice the asymmetry of the curves at higher SL (caused by these aural harmonics): a tone of given frequency f_0 more efficiently masks the higher frequencies than lower ones.

---

[6] Their addition, of course, also will contribute to a change in timbre (Chapter 4).

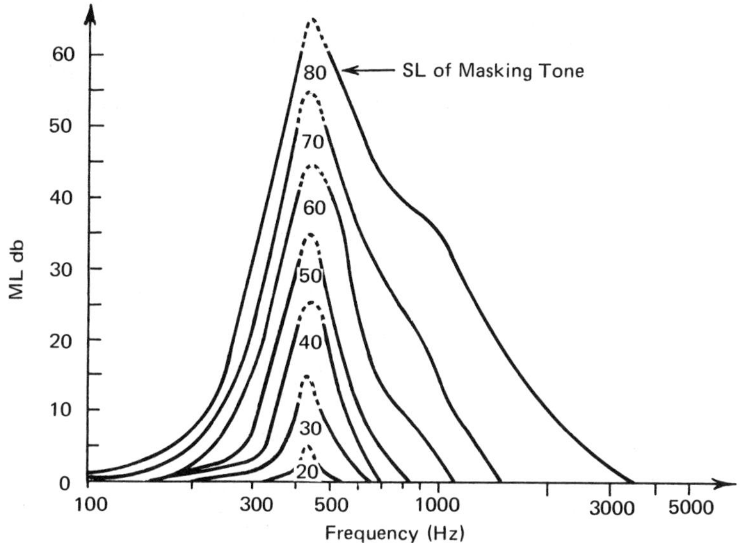

Fig. 3.14. Masking level corresponding to a pure tone of 415 Hz, for various sound level values (Egan and Hake 1950) of the masking tone. Reprinted by permission from the *Journal of the Acoustical Society of America*.

Masking plays an important role in polyphonic music, particularly in orchestration. On many occasions in musical scores, the participation of a given instrument such as an oboe or a bassoon may be totally irrelevant if it plays at the same time when the brasses are blasting a fortissimo. Likewise, the addition of flute stops or other soft string-like stops to a tutti of diapasons, mixtures, and reeds in the organ is completely irrelevant.

Finally, we must mention the effect of the *duration* of a tone on the loudness sensation. First of all, there is a *time threshold*—a minimum duration that a given pure sound must have in order to yield a tone sensation at all. This minimum duration is about 10–15 milliseconds, or at least 2–3 oscillation periods, if the frequency is below 50 Hz; tones lasting less than this are perceived as "clicks," not as "tones." Sounds lasting longer than 15 milliseconds (or 2–3 periods, whichever is longer) can be individualized as tones of given pitch and loudness.[7] Subjective loudness, however, does depend on tone duration (whereas pitch does not) (Plomp and Bouman 1959). The shorter the tone pulse, the lower its loudness, if the physical tone intensity (energy flow) is kept constant. When the tone duration is longer than about half a second,

---

[7] Quite generally, there is a physical principle which states that the frequency of a vibration cannot be defined more accurately than the *inverse of the total duration* of the vibration.

the loudness reaches a final value that is independent of duration (depending only on intensity).[8] Fig. 3.15 shows a sketch of the relative loudness decrease, or loudness attenuation, as a function of tone duration, and for different frequencies. Notice that the "final" response value

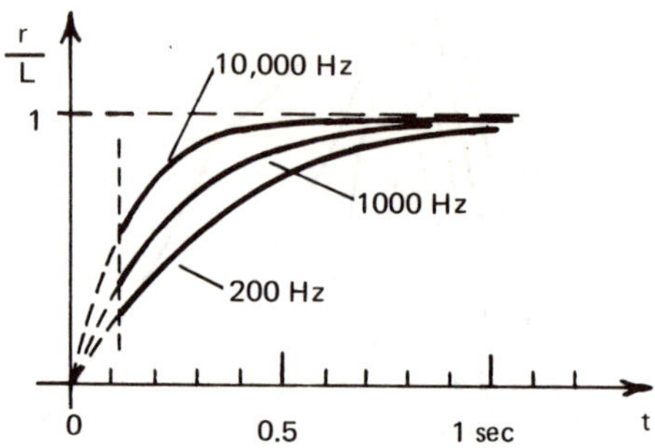

Fig. 3.15. Relative loudness of pure tones of short duration. r/L: ratio of actual loudness (r) to loudness (L) of a steady tone of the same frequency and amplitude.

is reached sooner for the higher frequencies. This has important implications for music: if we want to play a "staccato" passage on the piano at a given loudness level, say "forte," we must hit the keys much harder than if we were to play the same passage "legato," at the same loudness level.[9] This effect comes out much more pronounced with nondecaying tones, such as organ sounds. The organist has a considerable control of the subjective loudness of one given note by giving it just the right duration (phrasing). Masking (Fig. 3.14), too, depends on tone duration, for short tones. The masking threshold increases as the tone duration decreases, for tones lasting less than about 0.5 sec. For these short tones it is found that, in first approximation, the loudness sensation is not related to power flow (intensity), but to total acoustical *energy* delivered to the ear (intensity $\times$ duration). Actually, there are indications that it is related to the total number of *neural impulses* transmitted in association with the short tone, rather than with energy (Zwislocki 1969) (see the next section).

3.5 The Loudness Perception Mechanism and Related Processes

What physical or neural process is responsible for the difference between the limited subjective scale of loudness and the huge range

---

[8] For long exposure times an effect called *fatigue* sets in, decreasing again the subjective loudness sensation.

[9] For tones from musical instruments a complication arises: during tone buildup, which may last several tenths of seconds, a "natural" change in loudness and spectrum occurs at the source. Also, reverberation effects are important (Section 4.7).

of detectable intensities (Table 3.1; relation 3.17) of the original sound? In the case of primary pitch perception (Section 2.3) we already had encountered (without explicitly mentioning it) such a "compression": whereas the frequency scale ranges from about 20 Hz to about 16,000 Hz, this only comprises nine octaves of pitch. In that case the compression is mainly caused by the mechanical resonance properties of the cochlear partition: the curve in Fig. 2.8 indeed represents a roughly logarithmic relationship between the position x of the resonance region on the basilar membrane, and frequency.

In the case of the loudness detection mechanism, the "compression" is partly neural, partly mechanical. When a pure sound is present, the primary neurons connected to sensor cells located in the center of the region of maximum resonance amplitude increase their firing rate above the spontaneous level. This increase is a monotonic function of the stimulus amplitude, but not a linear one (See Chapter 4 of Flanagan 1972). Indeed, when the latter increases by a factor of, say, 100, (a 40 db increase in *SPL*, relation 3.16), the firing rate is found to increase only by a factor of 3–4. Another element contributing to loudness "compression" is related to the following: At higher *SPL*'s a primary neuron's firing rate *saturates* at a level that is only a few times that of spontaneous firing (the actual saturation level varying greatly from neuron to neuron). Any further increase in intensity would not alter greatly this firing rate; neurons simply cannot transmit pulses at a rate faster than the saturation value (determined by the refractory time after each pulse). How does one perceive a loudness increase even when the *SPL* surpasses the average neuron's saturation limit? What happens is that the more intense the sound wave is, the more extended the resonance region along the basilar membrane will be, hence the greater the *total number* of responding primary neurons whose thresholds are surpassed by the stimulus. In summary, an increase in intensity leads to an increase of the total number of transmitted impulses—either because the *firing rate of each neuron* has increased or because the *total number of activated neurons* has increased. This latter effect depends mainly on the shape of the membrane oscillation amplitude distribution—a purely mechanical property.

It follows from the previous discussion that the loudness sensation of a steady tone must be somehow related to the *total rate of neural impulses* triggered in the peripheral auditory system. As this neural information is transmitted to higher centers of the auditory tract and processed, the total firing rate gradually decreases (See Chapter 4 of Flanagan 1972). Typical acoustically evoked firing rates of cortical neurons are only 50–100 Hz. The relation between subjective loudness and total firing rate qualitatively explains the main properties of loudness summation (Section 3.4). For simultaneous tones of frequencies differing more than a critical band, the grand total of transmitted neural impulses is roughly equal to the sum of the pulse rates evoked by each component separately; hence, the total loudness will tend to be the sum of the *loudnesses* of each tone (relation 3.19). On the other hand, for tones whose frequencies lie within a critical band, with resonance regions on the basilar membrane overlapping substantially, the total number of pulses will be controlled by the sum of the original stimulus *intensities* (relation 3.18). This picture may, however, be complicated by another type of loudness coding: nerve fibers innervating the outer rows of hair cells are excited by less intense sounds than those contacting the inner row (Section 2.8). In other words, there may be a component of loudness coding that appears in the form of a *spatial* distribution of neural activity—as in the case of primary pitch coding.

The dependence of loudness sensation (and masking thresholds) with tone duration (Fig. 3.15) points to a *time-dependent buildup of the acoustical signal processing operation.* Only after several tenths of seconds does the neural mechanism reach a "steady state" of tone processing. It is important to emphasize again that (quite fortunately for music) during this buildup the pitch sensation is stable and unique from the beginning (except for the very early stage).

There is, however, a slight dependence of pitch with loudness, for a tone of constant frequency. For tones above about 1,000 Hz, pitch increases when loudness increases and vice-versa. Pitch matching experiments (Stevens 1934) have shown that this effect is small; considerable changes in intensity are required to lead to noticeable changes in pitch. This effect is probably due to the asymmetry of the distribution of excitation along the basilar membrane: a change in intensity causes a shift of the central point of excitation (even if the frequency remains constant), leading to a change in primary pitch sensation. This effect is of only marginal importance in music.

Here we come again to the question, formulated on page 31, concerning the primary pitch detection mechanism: if a pure tone of given intensity and frequency sets the basilar membrane into resonant oscillation covering a finite spatial range Δx, and primary pitch is encoded in the form of spatial position x of the activated fibers, how come only *one*, unique, sensation of pitch is produced? One might be tempted to invoke the periodicity pitch mechanism (Section 2.8) that codifies the information on repetition rate into volleys of nerve impulses in synchronism with the original pure tone stimulus (for a pure tone this repetition rate is indeed the same for all points of the basilar membrane within Δx). This, however, could only work in the low frequency range. Rather, the unique pitch sensation is believed to be the result of a *sharpening* or "lateral interaction" mechanism in the peripheral neural network (Houtgast 1972). This mechanism operates in other sensorial systems too, being responsible for particularly important effects of contrast enhancement (e.g., Mach bands) in vision (Ratliff 1972). It probably works as follows: impulses travelling up the afferent fibers that collect information from the hair cells lying in the stimulated region of the basilar membrane are branched off and conveyed to neighboring fibers through neurons which may act in either excitatory or inhibitory mode (Section 2.8). If the latter mode prevails, the transmission of signals from regions surrounding one of maximum stimulation is impaired, and the net result (after several stages of lateral interaction) would be a concentration or "funneling" of activity into a limited number of nerve fibers, surrounded by a ring of neural "quiet," or inhibition—thus leading to a unique sensation of primary pitch.[10] In general, this mechanism will enhance certain characteristic features of the spatial distribution of the original stimulus, such as maxima and abrupt changes. One must assume that information on the form of the vibration pattern leading to periodicity pitch and second order beat detection (Section 2.8) is preserved throughout the stages of lateral interaction. Indeed, it may come as an extra aid to the sharpening mechanism in the pitch determination at low frequencies.

In this sharpening mechanism, information is "funneled" from an initially large population of neurons to a considerably smaller number of units. It is thus possible to guess how the "neural quantum" effects mentioned on pages 23 and 72 may arise: noticeable changes in sensation may be determined by whether or not just *a few* more (or a few less) neurons are activated at some higher level in the auditory pathway. Since this activation is governed by the neurons' finite triggering thresholds (Section 2.8), a step-like behavior—the neural quantum—of the sensation would be the result.

Finally, it should be mentioned that in the peripheral neural network of the visual tract, neurons have been discovered that respond only to *time changes* of the original light stimulus (Hubel 1971). Since a similar behavior is expected for certain neurons in the auditory system, one might envisage the existence of a mechanism for direct coding of information on the *transient* characteristics of musical tones. A great deal of the corresponding neural processing may indeed already be done at the peripheral level of the cochlea (Lynn and Sayers 1970).

References

Egan, J. P., and H. W. Hake. 1950. On the masking pattern of a simple auditory stimulus. *J. Acoust. Soc. Am.* **22**:622.

Flanagan, J. L. 1972. *Speech Analysis, Synthesis and Perception.* 2nd ed. Springer-Verlag, New York.

Fletcher, H., and W. A. Munson. 1933. Loudness, its definition, measurement and calculation. *J. Acoust. Soc. Am.* **5**:82.

---

[10] It is not clear as yet if the efferent nerve bundle in the cochlea is the one that plays the inhibitory role in the lateral interaction mechanism.

Houtgast, T. 1972. Psychophysical evidence for lateral inhibition in hearing. *J. Acoust. Soc. Am.* **51**:1885.

Hubel, H. 1971. The visual cortex of the brain. In *Contemporary Psychology*. Readings from Scientific American. W. H. Freeman and Company, San Francisco.

Lynn, P. A., and B. McA. Sayers. 1970. Cochlear innervation, signal processing and their relation to auditory time-intensity effects. *J. Acoust. Soc. Am.* **47**:525.

Plomp, R., and M. A. Bouman. 1959. Relation between hearing threshold and duration for tone pulses. *J. Acoust. Soc. Am.* **31**:749.

Ratliff, F. 1972. Contour and contrast. *Sci. Am.* **226**(6):91.

Stevens, S. S. 1934. The attributes of tones. *Proc. US Natl. Acad. Sci.* **20**:457.

Stevens, S. S. 1955. Measurement of loudness. *J. Acoust. Soc. Am.* **27**:815.

Stevens, S. S. 1970. Neural events and the psychophysical law. *Science* **170**:1043.

Stevens, S. S. 1972. A neural quantum in sensory discrimination. *Science* **177**:749.

Zwicker, E., G. Flottorp, and S. S. Stevens. 1957. Critical bandwidth in loudness summation. *J. Acoust. Soc. Am.* **29**:548.

Zwislocki, J. J. 1969. Temporal summation of loudness: an analysis. *J. Acoust. Soc. Am.* **46**:431.

CHAPTER 4

GENERATION OF MUSICAL SOUNDS, COMPLEX TONES, AND THE PERCEPTION OF TONE QUALITY

In the preceding two chapters the two principal tonal attributes pitch and loudness have been analyzed, mainly on the basis of pure, single-frequency tones. These are not, however, the tones that play an active role in music. Music is made up of *complex* tones, each one of which consists of a superposition of pure tones blended together in a certain relationship so as to appear to our ear as unanalyzed wholes. A third fundamental tonal attribute thus emerges: tone quality, or timbre, related to the kind of mixture of pure sounds, or harmonic components, in a complex tone (Section 1.2).

Most musical instruments generate sound waves by means of vibrating strings or air columns. In Chapter 1 we called these the primary vibrating elements. The energy needed to sustain their vibration is supplied by an excitation mechanism and the final acoustical energy output in many instruments is controlled by a resonator. The room or concert hall in which the musical instrument is being played may be considered as a natural "extension" of the instrument itself, playing a substantial role in shaping the actual sound that reaches the ears of the listener.

In this chapter we shall discuss how real musical tones are actually produced in musical instruments, how they are made up as superpositions of pure tones, how they interact with the environment in the rooms or halls, and how all this leads to the perception of tone quality and instrument recognition.

4.1 Standing Waves in a String

We consider the case of a tense string, anchored at the fixed points P and Q (Fig. 4.1), of length L and mass per unit length d, stretched with a given force T that can be changed ad libitum, say, by changing

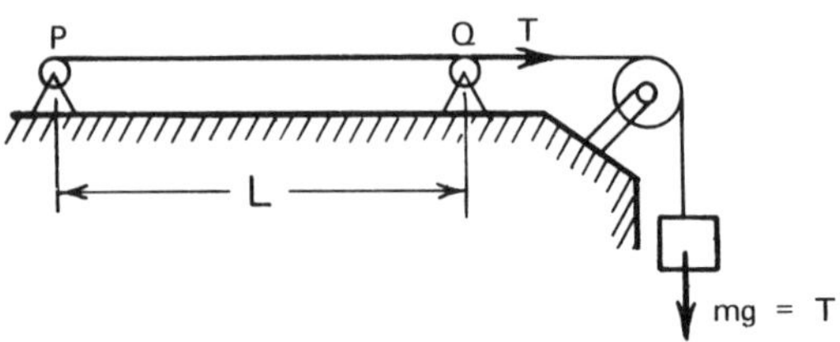

Fig. 4.1

the mass m of the body suspended from the string as shown in the figure. We now pluck or hit the string at a given point. Two transverse elastic wave pulses will propagate to the left and to the right away from the region of initial perturbation in a manner discussed in Section 3.2, with a velocity given by relation 3.3. These wave pulses, when reaching the fixed anchor points P and Q will be reflected; a positive or "upward" pulse will come back as a negative or "downward" pulse, and vice-versa. After a certain time (extremely short, in view of the high speed of the waves in a tense string), there will be waves simultaneously traveling back and forth in both directions along the string. In other words, we will have elastic wave energy "trapped" in the string between P and Q, these two points always remaining at rest. If there were no losses, this situation would remain so forever and the string would continue to vibrate indefinitely. However, friction and leaks through P and Q will eventually dissipate the stored energy and the waves will decay.[1] For the time being we shall ignore this dissipation.

In view of the discussion in Section 3.3, we realize that the above picture of waves traveling back and forth along a string strongly resembles the situation arising in a standing wave. Indeed, it can be shown mathematically that *standing waves are the only possible stable form of vibration for a string with fixed ends, with the anchor points P and Q playing the role of nodes.*

This has a very important consequence. Among all imaginable forms of standing waves, only those are possible for which nodes occur at P and Q. In other words, only those sinusoidal standing waves are permitted that "fit" an *integer number of times* between P and Q (Fig. 4.2), i.e., for which the length of the string L is an integer multiple of the distance between nodes l_N given by relation (3.13). Taking into account this relation we obtain the condition $L = n \, l_N = n\lambda/2$, where n is any integer number 1, 2, 3, ... This tells us that only the wavelengths

$$\lambda_n = \frac{2L}{n} \qquad n = 1, 2, 3, \ldots$$

(4.1)

---

[1] It is this energy "leak rate" through the "fixed" points (mainly the bridge) that is transformed into sound power in a string instrument's resonance body.

are permitted (Fig. 4.2). Using relation (3.8) we find that a string can only vibrate with the following frequencies:

$$f_n = \frac{1}{\lambda_n}\sqrt{\frac{T}{d}} = \frac{n}{2L}\sqrt{\frac{T}{d}} = nf_1 \qquad (4.2)$$

The lowest possible frequency is obtained for $n = 1$:

$$f_1 = \frac{1}{2L}\sqrt{\frac{T}{d}} \qquad (4.3)$$

This is called the *fundamental frequency* of the string. Note in (4.2) that all other possible frequencies are integer multiples of the funda-

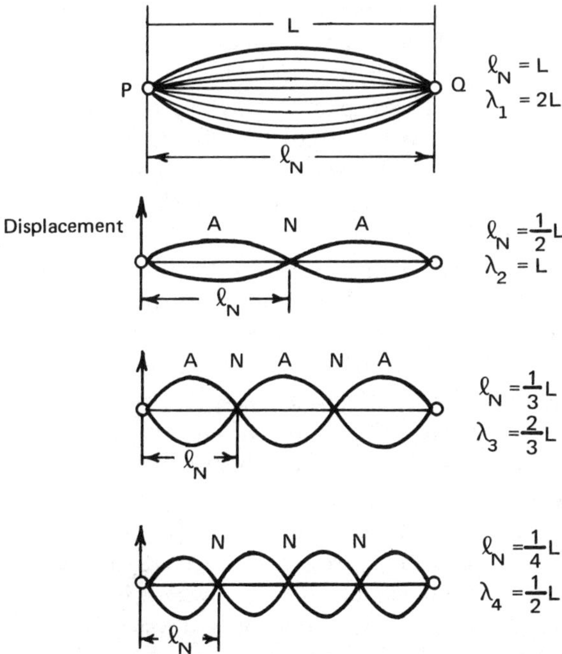

Fig. 4.2. Standing wave modes in a vibrating string.

mental frequency. They are called the upper *harmonics* of f_1 (Section 2.7). Notice in particular that the first harmonic ($n = 1$) is identical to the fundamental frequency; the second harmonic f_2 is the upper octave of f_1; the third harmonic is the twelfth (a fifth above the octave); the fourth harmonic the fifteenth (double octave); etc. (Fig. 4.3). The upper harmonics are also called *overtones*.[2]

____

[2] More precisely, *overtones* are the higher frequency components of a complex vibration, *regardless* of whether their frequencies are integer multiples of the fundamental frequency, or not.

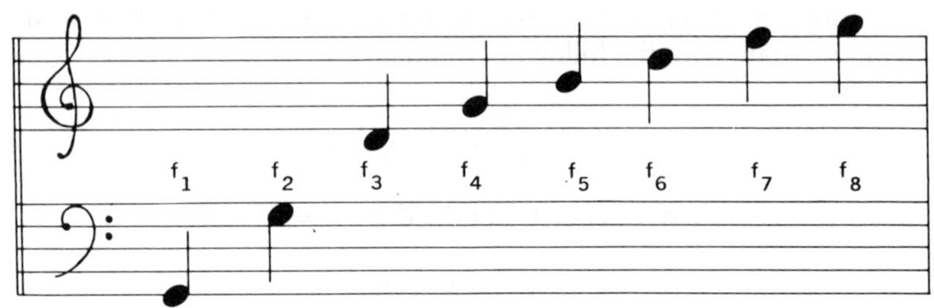

First Eight Harmonics of $f_1 = 98$ Hz (G_2)

Fig. 4.3

Relation (4.3) tells us that the fundamental frequency of oscillation of a string is proportional to the square root of the tension, and that it is inversely proportional to its length and to the square root of its mass per unit length. This explains many characteristic features of piano strings: for the upper part of the keyboard, strings become shorter and shorter (higher fundamental frequency f_1); if we have to tune a given string a little sharper, we have to increase the tension (higher f_1) and conversely; in the low pitch region, in order to save space and maximize power output, instead of increasing the length of a string, its mass per unit length d is increased (lower f_1) by surrounding it with a coil of additional wire. In the violin, where we have only four strings of nearly equal length, each one must have different tension and/or mass in order to bear a different basic pitch. In order to vary the fundamental frequency f_1 of a given string, one changes its vibrating length L by pressing the string against the fingerboard, thus introducing a node at the point of contact.

The appearance in a natural way of frequencies that are integer multiples of a fundamental frequency receives the name of "quantization" and plays a fundamental role everywhere in physics. The different possible discrete forms of vibration of a physical system are called its *modes* of vibration. The fundamental, the octave, the twelfth, etc., are the first, second, third, etc., modes of vibration of a tense string. All frequencies of the possible vibration modes of a string are given by relation (4.2). In this relation only quantities depending on the string appear; *the vibration modes are thus a permanent characteristic of the particular physical system.* In which of the possible modes will a given string *actually* vibrate? This is determined by the way how the vibrations are initiated, i.e., by the primary excitation mechanism. Because of the capability of linear superposition of waves, *many different modes may occur simultaneously without bothering each other.* In this section we focus our attention on how a string *can* vibrate. In the next one we shall examine the question of how a string actually *will* vibrate.

Let us consider the case of a vibrating string in which only *one* mode is excited. This can be accomplished easily in the laboratory by letting an alternating electrical current of a given frequency flow through a tense metal string, spanned through the gap of a strong permanent magnet. Magnetic forces on the current in the string will drive a transverse vibration at the frequency of the current. Whenever this frequency is near one of the string's harmonics, a large standing wave is produced; one can visually observe the nodes and antinodes (as sketched in Fig. 4.2), and clearly hear the sound produced (provided the string is mounted on a resonating box). The use of a stroboscope (a light source that flashes at a given, controllable frequency) enables one to "freeze" the shape of the string, or to observe it in "slow motion."

A more accessible and widely known experiment can be done with a piano. Press slowly, and then hold down, the key of a bass note, say G_2 (Fig. 4.3), so that no sound is produced (the hammer does not strike) but the damper remains lifted off that string. Then hit hard and "staccato" the key of the first upper octave (G_3). After that sound has stopped, you very clearly hear the G_2 string vibrating one octave higher: it has been excited (by resonance) in its second harmonic mode, G_3! Now repeat the same experiment hitting the twelfth (D_4) while holding down G_2: you hear the G_2 string vibrating in D_4. Continue with G_4, B_4, and so on. As a test, hit A_3 or F_3 while holding down G_2—there will be *no* effect: the G_2 string remains silent. The reason is that A_3 or F_3 are not upper harmonics of G_2, and the G_2 string simply cannot sustain stable vibrations at those frequencies.

Relation (4.2) really is only an approximate one, particularly for the higher order modes. The reason is that the speed of a transverse wave in a string *does* depend slightly on the frequency (or wavelength) of the wave (this is called *dispersion*) and expressions (3.3) and (3.8) are not entirely correct. Indeed, the wave velocity V_T is slightly larger than the value given by relation (3.3). This deviation increases with increasing distortion of the string, i.e., it becomes more important for smaller wavelengths and larger amplitudes. The result is that the frequencies of higher vibration modes of a piano string are slightly sharper than the values given by (4.2).[3] In general, when the frequencies of the higher modes of vibration of a system are not integer multiples of the fundamental frequency, we call these modes *inharmonic*. Vibrating solid bodies other than strings—e.g., xylophone bars, bells or chimes—have many inharmonic vibration modes, whose frequencies are not at all integer multiples of the fundamental frequency. In most of what follows, we shall assume, for simplicity, that the overtones of a vibrating string do coincide with the upper harmonics, and that relation (4.2) is exactly true.

---

[3] This does not affect greatly the pitch of the ensuing complex tone (Section 2.7). But it does affect tuning of the piano in the treble and bass register (when tuning is done by octaves).

4.2 Generation of Complex Standing Vibrations in String Instruments

There are two fundamental ways of exciting the vibration of a tense string: (1) a one-time energy supply by the action of striking (piano) or plucking (harpsichord, guitar); and (2) a continuous energy supply by the action of bowing (violin family). In both cases, the resulting effect is a *superposition of many vibration modes activated simultaneously*. In other words, individual musical sounds generated naturally by strings contain many different frequencies at the same time—those of the vibrating system's harmonics. Fig. 4.4 shows how this may arise

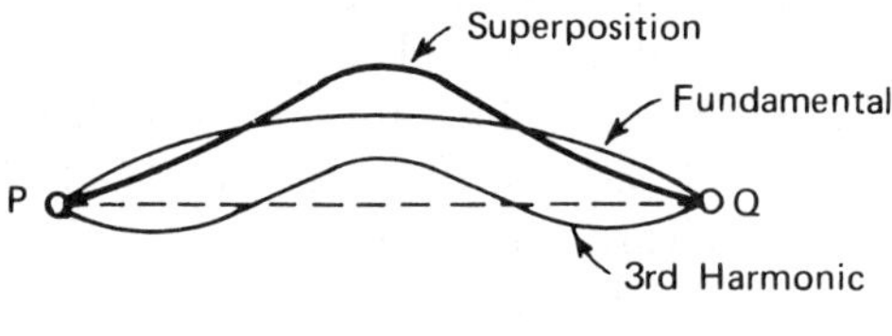

Fig. 4.4

in practice: adding the first and, say, the third harmonics, one obtains a resulting superposition that at a given instant of time, may look as depicted in this figure. Each mode behaves independently, and the instantaneous shape of the string is given by the superposition (sum) of the individual displacements, as dictated by each component separately. It is possible to use the previously mentioned experimental setup of a vibrating string in a magnetic field with an electric current flowing through it, this time using the combined output of *two* sinusoidal voltage generators whose frequencies are set equal to two of the string's harmonics, respectively. With the use of a stroboscope it is possible to clearly visualize the instantaneous shape of the string when it is vibrating in two modes at the same time. The relative proportion with which each overtone intervenes in the resulting vibration determines to a great extent (Sections 1.2, 4.8) the particular character, quality, or timbre of the generated tone. The pitch of a string's complex tone is determined by the fundamental frequency (4.3), as has been anticipated in Section 2.7.

A simple experiment with a piano convincingly shows that a string can indeed vibrate in more than one mode at the same time. Press down slowly, and hold, a given key (say G_2) (Fig. 4.3) so to lift the damper off the string. Then hit hard and staccato *simultaneously* D_4, G_4, B_4. After their sound disappeared, it is possible to clearly hear the G_2 string vibrate in all three modes simultaneously—we have one string alone sound a full G major triad! What happens is that three modes (third, fourth, and fifth harmonics) have been excited at roughly similar amplitudes (by resonance). A more drastic experiment is the following: hold the G_2 key down—and hit with your right underarm all black and white keys of two or more octaves above G_3—after the initial burst of noise has decayed, the G_2 string vibrates beautifully in the dominant seventh chord G_3, D_4, G_4, B_4, D_5, F_5, G_5, ... (Fig. 4.3). Any of the other sounded notes could neither excite nor entertain a stable vibration on the G_2 string.

Whereas the above experiment shows that a given piano string *can* vibrate simultaneously in different modes at the same time, the following experiment shows that a piano string, sounded normally, actually *does* vibrate in many harmonic modes. Pick again a bass note, say, G_2. But this time press the G_3 key down slowly without sounding it, and keep it down. Then sound a loud, staccato G_2. The G_3 string starts vibrating in its own fundamental mode (i.e., G_3). The reason is that this mode has been excited (through resonance) by the *second* harmonic of the vibrating G_2 string. If instead of G_2 you had sounded A_2, the G_3 string would have remained silent. Then repeat the same experiment several times, successively pressing silently the keys of D_4, G_4, B_4, D_5, ... etc. Each one of them will be excited by the corresponding upper harmonic mode of the G_2 string.[4]

Many vibration modes appear together when a string is set into vibration. What determines *which* ones and *how much* of each? This is initially controlled by the particular way the string is set into vibration, i.e., by the primary excitation mechanism. Depending on how and where we hit, pluck, or bow the string, different mixtures of overtones and, hence, different qualities of the ensuing sound will be obtained. We may explain this on the basis of the following examples. Assume that we give a string the initial form shown in Fig. 4.5a (this would be

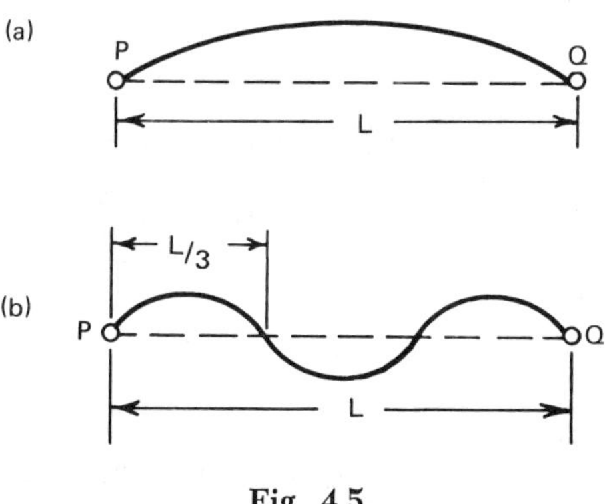

Fig. 4.5

<hr>

[4] The main objective of the *pedal* mechanism of the piano is based on this phenomenon: pressing the pedal lifts *all* dampers, and the strings are let free to vibrate by resonance. When one given note is sounded, all those strings will be induced to vibrate that belong to the series of harmonics of that note.

rather difficult to accomplish in practice, though). Since the shape more or less conforms to the fundamental mode (Fig. 4.2), the string will indeed start vibrating in that mode when it is released. If now the initial form is that shown in Fig. 4.5b, the string would vibrate in the third mode when released (Fig. 4.2). But what will happen if the initial shape has the far more realistic form of Fig. 4.6, which is obtained

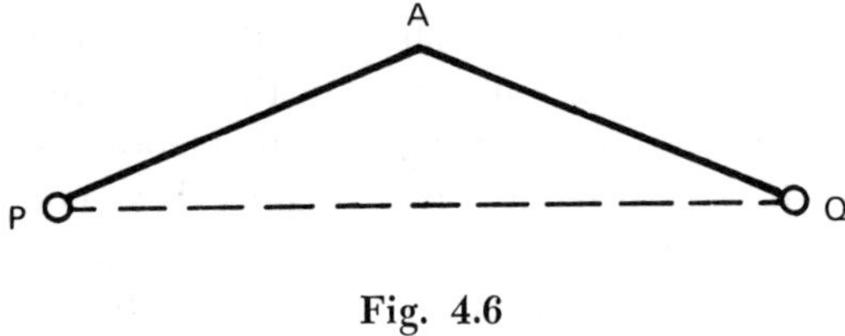

Fig. 4.6

when we pluck the string at the midpoint A between P and Q? To find out let us superpose, i.e., add linearly, the cases of Figs. 4.5a and b. We obtain the shape shown in Fig. 4.7a which resembles rather well that of the initial configuration of a plucked string (Fig. 4.6). We thus anticipate that the fundamental mode and at least the third harmonic should be simultaneously present in the vibration of a string plucked

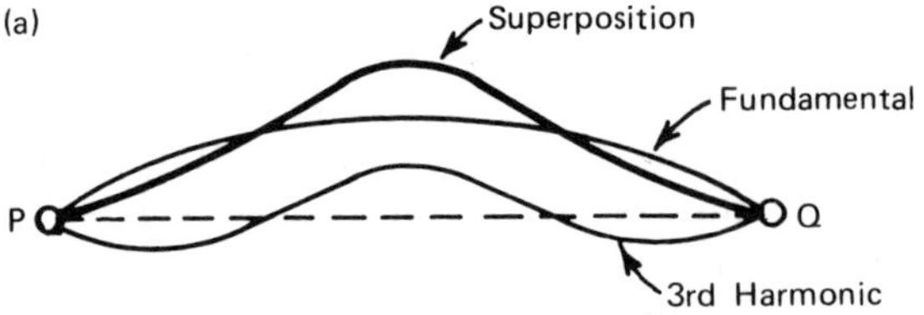

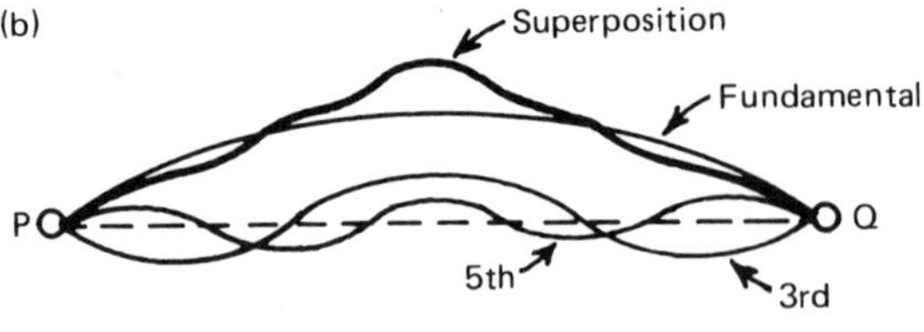

Fig. 4.7

at the midpoint. We can improve greatly the approximation to the shape of Fig. 4.6 by adding more higher harmonics in appropriate proportions (Fig. 4.7b). One can iron out the remaining wiggles shown in this figure by just adding more and more higher harmonics in appropriate proportion until the wanted shape is almost exactly reproduced.

A remarkable fact is that there is no guesswork involved in all this:

it can be accomplished in rigorously mathematical form! In fact, it can be shown that *any arbitrary initial shape of a string can be reproduced to an arbitrary degree of accuracy by a certain superposition of geometrical shapes corresponding to the string's harmonic vibration modes* (standing waves). It is this "mathematical" superposition of shapes, in particular, the proportion of their amplitudes and phases, which defines the physical superposition of harmonics with which the string will actually vibrate when it is released from its initial configuration. In other words, each one of the component standing waves, which when added together make up the initial form of the string (e.g., Fig. 4.7b), proceeds vibrating in its own way with its own characteristic frequency and amplitude once the string is released. As time goes on, the instantaneous form of the string changes periodically in a complicated way; but every time a fundamental period $\tau_1 = 1/f_1$ has elapsed, all component modes will find themselves in the same relationship as in the beginning, and the string will have the same shape as it had initially. It is very important to remark here that the initial configuration of the string determines not only the amplitudes of the harmonic vibration modes but also their phases (relative timings). The point at which the string is plucked will determine the particular proportion of upper harmonics, i.e., the initial quality of the sound emitted (Section 1.2). If we pluck at the center, we will have the situation shown in Fig. 4.7b, and only *odd* harmonics will appear. On the other hand, the closer to the fixed extremes we pluck, the richer the proportion of upper harmonics will be. In general, all those harmonics that have a node at the plucking point will be surpressed (e.g., all even harmonics in the example of Fig. 4.6), whereas those having an antinode there will be enhanced. This effect is most efficiently exploited by the harp player to control the timbre of his instrument's sound.

In a string that is set in vibration by plucking, we have a situation in which the primary excitation mechanism initially gives a certain *potential energy* to the system, by deforming the string. After release, this initial energy is periodically converted back and forth into kinetic energy of vibration (Section 3.1). On the other hand, when a string is set into vibration by striking, a certain amount of *kinetic energy* is initially provided by the striking mechanism (e.g., the hammer in the piano), setting the points of the initially undeformed string in motion. This initial energy is then periodically converted into potential energy of deformation. It can be shown mathematically that *from the knowledge of the initial velocities of the points of the struck string, the ensuing superposition of harmonics can be deduced.* Thus, a string hit at the midpoint will oscillate principally with the fundamental frequency, plus a mixture of decreasing intensities of the odd harmonics. The closer to the end points P or Q a string is struck, the richer in upper harmonics the tone will be. As it happened with the plucked string, harmonics whose nodes are at or near the striking point will be excluded, and those having an antinode there will be enhanced.

When a string is set into vibration by plucking or striking, we observe the vibration to decay away quite rapidly. This is due to the action of dissipative forces: elastic friction inside the string and, most importantly, forces that set into small vibratory motion whatever is holding the string in place at its end points. Only part of this energy loss is actually converted into sound wave energy. A freely vibrating string mounted on a rigid, heavy frame produces only a faint sound: most of the vibration energy disappears forever in form of frictional energy (heat). The conversion into sound wave energy can be greatly increased by mounting the string on a board of special elastic properties, called a *resonator* (sound board in the piano, the body of a violin). In that case the end points of the string are allowed to vibrate a tiny bit (so little that, as compared to the rest of the string vibrations, these end points technically still function as nodes), and the energy of the string can be gradually converted into vibration energy of the board. Due to the usually quite large surface of this board, this energy is then converted with greater efficiency into sound wave energy. The resulting sound is much louder than in the case of a rigidly mounted string—but *it decays much faster*, because of the considerably increased *rate* at which the available amount of string energy is spent (power, Section 3.1).

Let us examine the process of vibration decay in more detail. For simplicity we consider a string that has been set into free vibration in its fundamental mode only. We focus our attention on the gradually decreasing amplitude of the oscillation of the string, say, at an antinodal point. Measurements show that, for a given string, damped oscillations with larger amplitude decay at a faster rate than those with smaller amplitude. The resulting motion is shown in Fig. 4.8. Notice the slope of the "envelope" curve, which decreases as the amplitude decreases. This is called an *exponential* decay of amplitude. Most important (and quite fortunately for music!), the frequency of a damped oscillation remains constant.

This is roughly the way a string behaves when it vibrates freely in one given mode after it is struck or plucked. If it is mounted on a rigid board the energy loss will be relatively small and so will be the amplitude damping (Fig. 4.9a). If, instead, it is mounted on a sound board, it will give away energy at a larger rate by setting the board and the surrounding air into oscillation. The oscillations will thus decay faster (Fig. 4.9b).

A characteristic quantity is the so-called *decay half-time*. This is the time interval after which the amplitude of the oscillations has been reduced to one-half the initial value (Fig. 4.8). The remarkable fact of an exponential decay is that this half-time is always the same through-

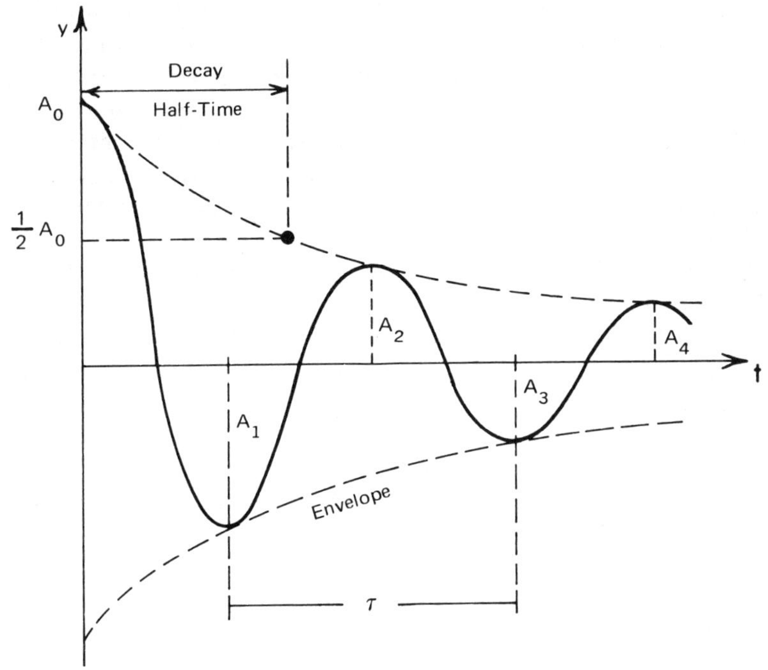

Fig. 4.8

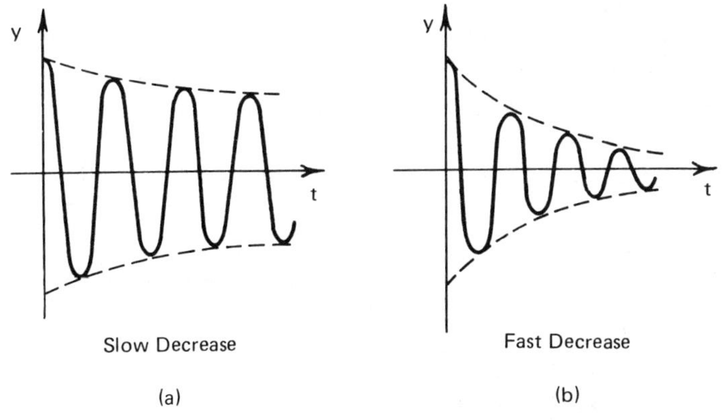

Fig. 4.9

out the decay: it takes the same time to halve the amplitude, no matter what the actual value of the latter is. The decay half-time is thus a characteristic constant of a damped oscillation. The typical decay half-time of a piano string is about 0.4 seconds.

When a string vibrates in several modes at the same time, the situation is more complex. However, we still find that *each mode* decays exponentially, only that the decay half-time will be different for different modes. The resulting complex sound thus not only decreases in loudness, but also its quality will gradually change. In the piano strings the lower frequency modes decay faster than the upper harmonics; in a vibrating bell the opposite happens and the lower harmonics continue to sound after the upper ones have decayed away. Otherwise, the overall behavior of a freely vibrating string is exclusively determined by the way in which the vibration has been initially excited (hit or plucked string). In the piano, for instance, that is controlled exclusively *by the speed with which the hammer hits*—nothing else. In the case of a *single* tone the so-called piano "touch" is nothing but plain loudness with a timbre that is irrevocably coupled to that loudness and to the subsequent decay. Tone quality cannot be controlled independently. The "touch" that undoubtedly exists when a musical piece (i.e., a sequence and/or superposition of tones) is played is related to other psychoacoustical effects (mainly tone *duration* control, small variations of loudness from tone to tone, and *nonsimultaneity* of the different notes of a chord).

What can we do in order to avoid the damping of a string vibration? Obviously, we must compensate the energy loss by somehow supplying extra energy to our vibrating system at a rate equal to the dissipated power. If the supplied power *exceeds* the energy loss rate by a certain amount, the amplitude will gradually build up. But this buildup would not go on indefinitely: while the power supply remains constant, the power dissipation will increase as the amplitude increases, and a regime will eventually be attained in which the dissipated power has become equal to the supplied power (Fig. 4.10). This happens during the tone buildup of any instrument of continuous sounding capability (bowed violin string, flute, organ pipe, etc.). In such a case each harmonic is found to build up independently, as if there were an individual power

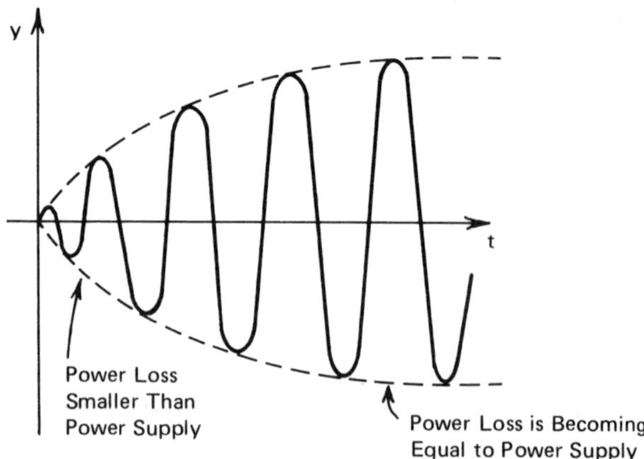

Fig. 4.10

supply mechanism for each mode. The larger this power supply, the larger, of course, will be the final intensity level.

The bowing mechanism is a good example of how string oscillations can be sustained in a constant regime. The physical problem is mathematically complicated and can be treated only after making several simplifying assumptions (Friedlander 1953; Keller 1953). Here we can only give a qualitative description of the theory. The interaction between the bow and the string is produced by forces of friction. Quite generally, we distinguish two types of frictional interaction. The first is the so-called *static* friction that arises when there is *no displacement* between the interacting bodies. This happens when the string "sticks" to the bow, thus moving with the same speed as the latter (or, in more familiar terms, when you try to push a heavy table while it "sticks" to the floor). The second type is *dynamic* friction, arising when the two interacting bodies (their contact surfaces) are *sliding* against each other. This happens when the string "snaps back" and moves in the opposite direction as that of the bow (and happens while you continue to push a table *after* it had started moving). Dynamic friction is weaker than static friction; both mechanisms are controlled by the force, perpendicular to the surface of contact, with which one body presses against the other (and vice-versa). In the case of a bowed string, this perpendicular force is called the *bowing pressure*—a dreadful name in the ears of a physicist, because it is *not* a pressure, just a force.

Let us now consider an idealized situation: a very, very long string, bowed at a point A with an infinitesimally thin bow (Fig. 4.11). The bow moves with a speed b in the upward direction. Let us furthermore assume that right from the beginning (time t_0) the string sticks to the bow. This means that the point of contact A (we really should say the surface of contact) also moves upward with the same speed b. The result will be a deformation of the string in the form of a transverse wave that will propagate away from point A as shown in Fig. 4.11 for

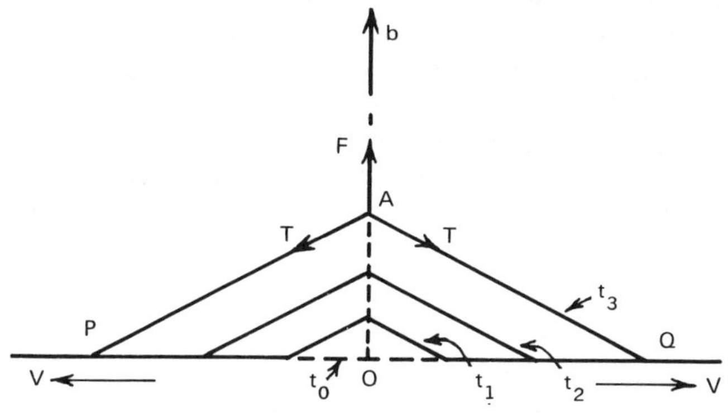

Fig. 4.11

various instants of time t_1, t_2, t_3. Since transverse waves propagate with a speed V, given by relation (3.3), which happens to be much higher than any reasonable bowing speed b, the slope b/V of the kinked portions of the string AP, AQ will in reality be extremely small. Under these conditions, the transverse force F applied by the bow (not to be confused with the bowing pressure which would be directed *perpendicular* to the paper) holds the balance with the projections along OA of both tension forces T. This means that $F = 2T\,b/V$. In order to actually have a regime of static friction, with the string sticking to the bow, the force F must be less than a certain threshold F_s, called the limit of static friction. Experimental results show that this limit is proportional to the bowling "pressure": $F_s = \mu_s P$. μ_s (Greek letter mu) is the *coefficient of static friction;* it depends on the "roughness" of the contact surfaces (in this case, on the amount of rosin on the bow's hairs). The condition for "sticking" is then $F = 2T\,b/V < \mu_s P$.[5] Likewise, the condition for slipping will be $F = 2T\,b/V > \mu_s P$. Since the quantities V, T, and μ_s are constant parameters for a given string, we may summarize both expressions in the following, more physical way:

Quantity control- *lable by the player*	*Quantity fixed* *for each string*	*Type of string motion* *with respect to the bow*
	$< \dfrac{\mu_s V}{2T}$	sticking
$\dfrac{b}{P}$		
	$> \dfrac{\mu_s V}{2T}$	slipping

$$(4.4)$$

Notice in relations (4.4) that what matters is the *ratio* of bow velocity to bow pressure, not b or P alone. The ratio b/P thus defines the nature of the motion of the bowed string.

What now, if the string is slipping from the very beginning? [bottom relation in (4.4)]. In that case the speed v of the bowing point A of the string will be less than (or may even be oppositely directed to) the speed of the bow, b. We have a regime of *dynamic* friction, in which it turns out that the force $F = 2T\,b/V$ (Fig. 4.11), while still proportional to P, now also depends on the *relative speed* $b - v$ between bow and string (speed of slipping). We write this in the form $F = \mu_D P$, where μ_D is the coefficient of *dynamic friction*, which now depends on the relative velocity $b - v$ (is a *function* of $b - v$). Thus, during the slipping regime:

$$\frac{b}{P} = \mu_D \frac{V}{2T} \tag{4.5}$$

If we knew the dependence of μ_D with the speed of slipping $b - v$,

---

[5] $<$ means "less than," $>$ means "greater than."

we could use expression (4.5) to determine the speed v of the contact point A of the string. Again, this relation is governed by the ratio b/P. But notice carefully: what is determined by this ratio is the difference $b - v$, i.e., the speed of the string *as seen by the bow*. The larger b is, the larger will be v, for a given value of b/P. While this ratio determines the *nature* of the string motion [sticking vs. slipping, relations (4.4)], the bow speed determines the actual speed of the string (for a given b/P). Thus if one increases bow speed, but *at the same time* increases bow pressure so to hold their ratio constant, the nature of the string motion will not change at all—only its velocity will increase linearly with b. This will lead to an increase of the amplitude, i.e., intensity of sound, in the real case. In other words: *the amplitude of the vibration of a bowed string (loudness of the tone) is solely controlled by the bow velocity, but in order to maintain constant the nature or type of the string motion (quality of the tone), one must keep the bowing pressure proportional to the bowing speed.* This is well known by string instrument players, who increase both bow speed b and bowing pressure P at the same time to produce an increase in loudness *without* a change of timbre; or who increase b and *decrease* P, to produce an increase in loudness *with* change in timbre.

Although relations (4.4 and 5) had been derived for an "infinitely" long string, these results are still true for the "real" case of a string of finite length. Let us now consider a little more realistic case: a string of finite length L, bowed with an infinitesimally thin bow at the midpoint O (Fig. 4.12). In this figure we show schematically the shape of the

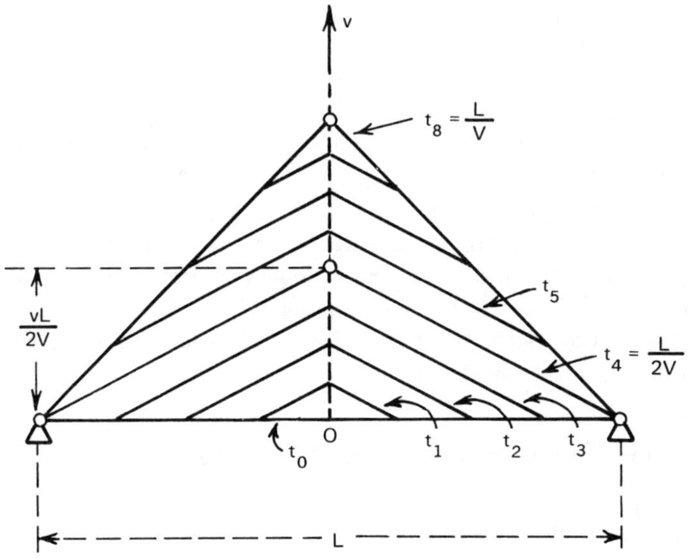

Fig. 4.12

string as we start bowing (again, the slopes are *highly* exaggerated). v is the speed of the midpoint [we may either have slipping $(v < b)$, or sticking $(v = b)$]. Notice that at time $t_4 = L/2V$ the first "wave" (of slope v/V) has reached the string's end points. There, the wave is reflected and superposed with the ongoing initial wave, unfolding the "kinked" shape shown for the times t_5 to t_7. Then, at $t_8 = L/V$ something new happens (Fig. 4.12): *the slope suddenly changes at the bowing point.* This changes the expression for the force F and a new regime may arise (e.g., slipping, if previously there was sticking). We cannot continue this discussion without running into considerable mathematical complexities (Keller 1953). Just notice that these crucial changes in shape (whenever the wave is reflected at the fixed end points) always occur at times that are *integer multiples* of L/V, a quantity that is completely independent of the bowing mechanism. Actually, the inverse of L/V appears in the expression (4.3) of the fundamental frequency of the vibrating string. The reader may thus envisage how that frequency (and all upper harmonics) may indeed be excited (and maintained) by the bowing mechanism. He may also infer from Fig. 4.12 (with a little extra imagination) that in its real vibratory motion, *a bowed string always has an instantaneous shape that is made up of sections of straight lines;* this result has been verified experimentally long ago. A study of the energy balance in the bowing mechanism reveals that most of the energy given to the string by the bow during the "sticking" portions of the motion is spent in the form of frictional heat (work of the dynamic friction force) during the slipping phases. Only a small fraction is actually converted into sound energy!

As in the case of a plucked or struck string, the particular mixture of harmonic modes of vibration will depend on the position of the bowing point. Bowing close to the bridge will enhance the upper harmonics and make the tone "brighter"; bowing closer to the string's midpoint (closer to the fingerboard), the intensity of upper harmonics is considerably reduced and the sound is "softer."

In the previous discussion we have tacitly assumed that the bow is being displaced exactly perpendicular to the string. If it has a small component of parallel motion, *longitudinal* vibration modes of the string can be excited. Their frequency is much higher than the fundamental frequency of the transverse modes; they are responsible for the squeaky sounds heard in beginners' play.

4.3 Sound Vibration Spectra and Resonance

When a string vibrates in a series of different modes at the same time, the generated sound waves are complex, too. Each harmonic component of the original string vibration contributes with its own share to the resulting sound wave, of frequency equal to that of the corresponding mode and of intensity and phase that are related to the intensity and phase of the latter through the intervening transformation processes. The result is a superposition of sound waves blended together into one complex wave, of fundamental frequency f_1 [equal to the fundamental frequency of the vibrating element (4.3)] and with a series of upper harmonics of frequencies $2f_1$, $3f_1$, $4f_1$, ... etc. The resulting vibration is periodic, repeating with a period equal to $\tau_1 = 1/f_1$. In other words, the fundamental frequency f_1 also represents the repetition rate of the resulting complex vibration (Section 2.7). The shape of the resulting curve depends on *what* harmonics are present, on *how much* there is of each (i.e., on their relative amplitudes), and on their *relative timing* (i.e., their relative phases).

And here we come to a mathematical theorem that has had an absolutely smashing impact on practically every branch of physics—in particular, physics of music. In short, the theorem states that *any periodic vibration,* however complicated, *can be represented as the superposition of pure harmonic vibrations,* whose fundamental frequency is given by the repetition rate of the periodic vibration. But that is not all: this theorem also provides all mathematical "recipes" for the numerical determination of the amplitudes and phases of the upper harmonic components! It is called Fourier's theorem, named after a famous 19th-century French mathematician. The determination of the harmonic components of a given complex periodic motion is called *Fourier analysis;* the determination of the resultant complex periodic motion from a given set of harmonic components is called *Fourier synthesis.* Similarly, given a complex tone, the process of finding the harmonic components is called *sound analysis.* Conversely, given a group of harmonic components, the operation of blending them together to form a complex tone is called *sound synthesis.*

Let us discuss one example of Fourier analysis. Of course, we cannot give here the whole mathematical operation that is needed to obtain the numerical results; we will have to accept these and, rather, concentrate on their physical interpretation. We pick the periodic motion shown in Fig. 4.13, corresponding to a "saw-tooth" wave. τ is the period,

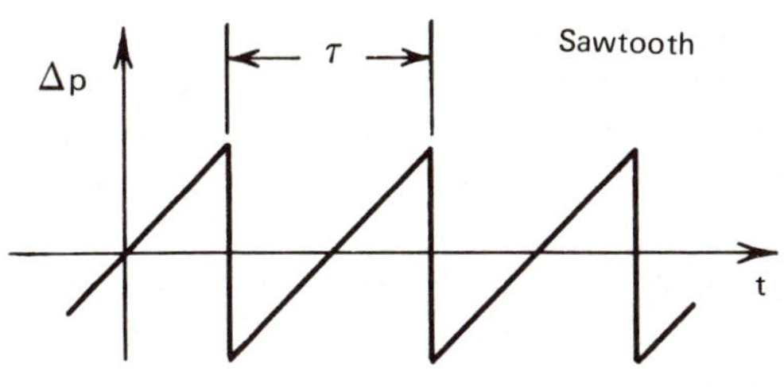

Fig. 4.13

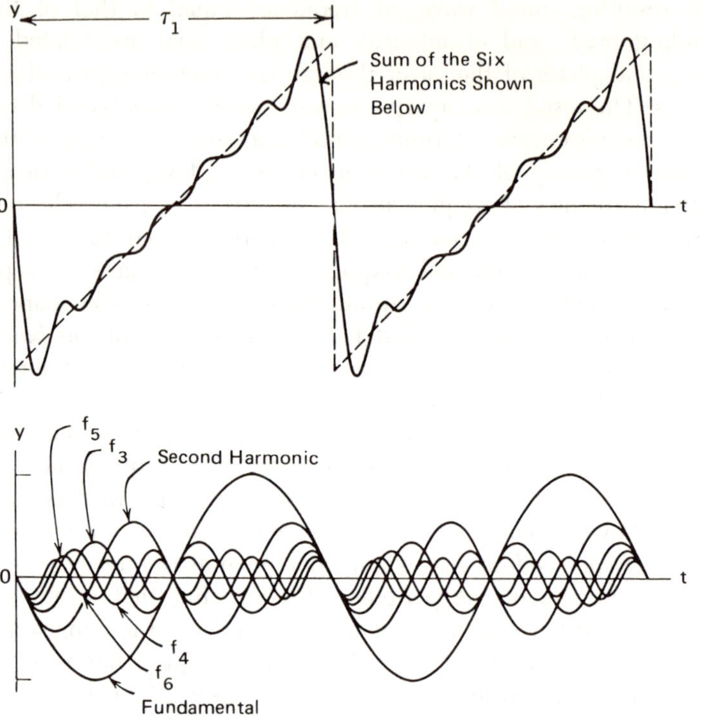

Fig. 4.14. Fourier analysis (up to the 6-th harmonic) of a sawtooth wave.

$f_1 = 1/\tau$ the repetition rate or fundamental frequency. This type of vibration can be generated electronically. To some extent it represents in an idealized form the motion of a bowed string. Fig. 4.14 shows how this periodic motion can be made up of pure, harmonic vibrations. Of course, many wiggles still remain in the curve corresponding to the sum. But this is due to the fact that, for better clarity, we have stopped adding after only the sixth harmonic. Adding more and more upper harmonics (of amplitude and phase obtained by the method of Fourier analysis) will iron out these wiggles and the sawtooth shape will be approached more and more closely. Observe attentively the relative amplitudes and the relative timing of the harmonic components, and how positive and negative portions add up to give the resultant curve. With a trained eye and intuition it is possible to predict qualitatively the principal harmonic components of a periodic motion of almost any, arbitrary, shape.

We now have to find a way to characterize physically a given complex sound. In principle, we must specify *three distinct series of quantities:* the frequencies of the harmonic components, the pressure variation amplitudes or intensities of the components, and their phases or relative timings (e.g., Fig. 2.5). In practice, however, it is customary to specify only the fundamental frequency f_1, and the intensities of the harmonic components, because, first, it is understood that all upper frequencies are just integer multiples of the fundamental frequency f_1, and second, the phases of the components play only a secondary role in timbre perception, particularly for the first (and most important) half-dozen or so harmonics (Section 4.8).

The sequence of intensity values I_1, I_2, I_3, ... , of the harmonic components of a complex tone represents what is called the *spectrum* of the tone. Two complex tones of the same pitch and loudness but different spectrum sound differently, i.e., have a different tone quality. The difference in spectrum gives us an important cue to distinguish between tones from different instruments—but other clues, particularly tone attack and decay, are also needed for instrument identification (Section 4.8). The fact that a multiplicity of physical parameters (I_1, I_2, I_3, ...) is related to tone quality indicates that the latter is a *multidimensional* psychophysical magnitude.

Tone spectra can be represented graphically by plotting for each harmonic frequency (horizontal axis) the intensity with which that harmonic component intervenes (vertical axis) (e.g., Fig. 4.16). Quite often, values of *SL* (3.15) or *SPL* (3.16) are used instead of intensities to represent a spectrum. Also, intensity or *SL* values *relative* to that of the fundamental, or relative to the total intensity $I = I_1 + I_2 + I_3 + ...$, are used. There are many books where sound spectra of actual musical instruments are reproduced (e.g., Culver 1956). A word of caution is necessary, though. From a psychophysical point of view, a conventional harmonic (Fourier) representation of a tone spectrum makes no real sense beyond the sixth or seventh harmonic, because in that range neighboring components start falling within a critical band. Since this is the elementary acoustical information-collection and -integration unit of the ear (Section 2.4), the auditory system could not resolve the individual intensities of these upper harmonics [case (1) on p. 79]. A psychophysically more meaningful representation of tone spectra is obtained by listing the integrated intensity values *per critical band* (frequency intervals of roughly ⅓-octave extension).

Only steady tones can be "resolved" into a superposition of harmonics of discrete frequencies that are integer multiples of the fundamental. When a vibration pattern is *changing* in time, this is not possible anymore. However, a sort of "expanded version" of Fourier analysis is applicable. It can be shown mathematically that a time-dependent tone leads to a *continuous spectrum* in which all frequencies are represented, with a given intensity for each infinitesimal frequency interval. If the tone is *slowly* time-dependent, discrete frequencies (those of the harmonics) still will be represented with highest intensity (spectral "peaks"), but if the time change is appreciable from cycle to cycle;

the discrete character will disappear and the spectrum will tend to become a continuous curve covering the full frequency range (even if the tone was originally pure). This fact leads to another important observation concerning "high fidelity" reproducing equipment (see also p. 36). We noted in Section 1.2, and will come back to this in Section 4.8, that *transients*, i.e., rapid time variations of the vibration pattern of a tone play a determining role in the perception of quality or timbre. Thus, in order to reproduce the transients of a given tone correctly, the recording and reproducing systems must leave the tone spectrum undistorted *over the full frequency range*. Our ear does not need the frequency components lying much over about 5,000 Hz of a steady tone, but the reproducing system needs them to give us a correct version of the rapidly changing portions of a tone!

The sound spectrum of a string instrument is not at all equal to that of the vibrations of the strings. The reason lies in the frequency-dependent efficiency of the *resonator* (sound board of a piano, body of the violin), whose main function is to extract energy from the vibrating string at an enhanced rate and convert it more efficiently into sound wave power. As mentioned earlier, the string vibrations are converted into vibrations of the resonator in a process in which the "fixed" end points of the string (particularly the one situated on the bridge) are allowed to vibrate a tiny bit. This remnant vibration is so small that it does not invalidate the fact that, from the string's point of view, these points still are vibration nodes. In spite of being so small, these vibrations *do* involve an appreciable energy transfer.[6] The explanation is found in the very definition of work (Section 3.1): although the displacement of the string's end points is extremely small, the *forces* applied on them are large (of the order of the tension of the string), so that the *product* force times displacement (work) may be quite appreciable. Owing to the large surface of a typical resonator, conversion of its vibration energy into sound wave energy is very efficient—thousands or even millions of times more efficient than the direct conversion of vibrating string energy into sound.

Like a string, the complex elastic structure of a piano soundboard or body of a violin has preferred modes of oscillation. In this case, however, there is no such simple integer multiple relationship between the associated frequencies as given in relation (4.2). Moreover, there are so many modes with nearly overlapping frequencies that one obtains a whole continuum of preferred vibration frequencies, rather than discrete values.[7] Let us briefly discuss how these vibration modes arise.

---

[6] The function of the *mute*, when it is applied to the bridge of a string instrument, is to decrease this energy transfer for the higher frequency components, thus altering the quality of the resulting tone.

[7] Neither does a *real* string, of *finite* thickness, have "sharp," discrete modes of oscillation.

To that effect, instead of considering the violin body as a whole, we examine the vibration of just one of the plates of the body. To find out the possible vibration modes it is necessary to excite the plate with a sinusoidal, single-frequency mechanical vibrator, at a given point of the plate (e.g., with which the bridge is normally in contact). Elastic waves propagate in two dimensions away from the excitation point and are reflected at the edges of the plate. The only stable modes of vibration are standing waves compatible with the particular boundary conditions of the plate. This process is highly complicated, impossible to treat mathematically. In the laboratory, however, it is possible to make the vibrations of the plate visible through a modern laser technique called holography (Reinicke and Cremer 1970). The simplest mode of oscillation (called "ring mode") is one in which the central region of the plate moves sinusoidally up and down, with the boundary acting as a nodal line. The ring modes of the violin plates determine the "tap tone," the sound that is evoked by tapping the body.

The vibration response of a resonator to a given signal of *fixed* amplitude (either from a mechanical vibrator, or from a vibrating string mounted on that resonator) depends strongly on the frequency of the primary oscillations. For that reason, a soundboard reacts differently to vibrations of different frequency. Some frequencies will be preferentially enhanced whereas others may not be amplified at all. A frequency for which the energy conversion is especially efficient is called a *resonance frequency* of the resonator. A resonator may have many different resonance frequencies; they may be well-defined ("sharp" resonance) or spread over a broad range of frequencies. The graph obtained by plotting the output signal (for instance, as measured by the intensity of the emerging sound wave) as a function of the frequency of a sinusoidal input vibration of constant amplitude, is called a *resonance curve*, or response curve. Usually, the intensity of the output signal I is represented in relation to some given reference signal I_{ref}, and expressed in *decibels* (Section 3.4):

$$R = 10 \log \frac{I}{I_{ref}} \qquad \text{(in decibels)} \qquad (4.6)$$

R is the value of the response function. The dependence of R with frequency gives the above-mentioned resonance curve. Fig. 4.15 is an example, corresponding to the body of a violin (Hutchins and Fielding 1968). Some of the lower frequency peaks correspond to the vibration modes of the air enclosed in the body. The first sharp rise marked in Fig. 4.15 corresponds to the tap tone of the body.[8] All other resonances correspond to more complicated vibration modes. The response curve

____

[8] The position (in frequency) and the shape of this particular resonance peak is of capital importance for the quality of a string instrument (Hutchins and Fielding 1968).

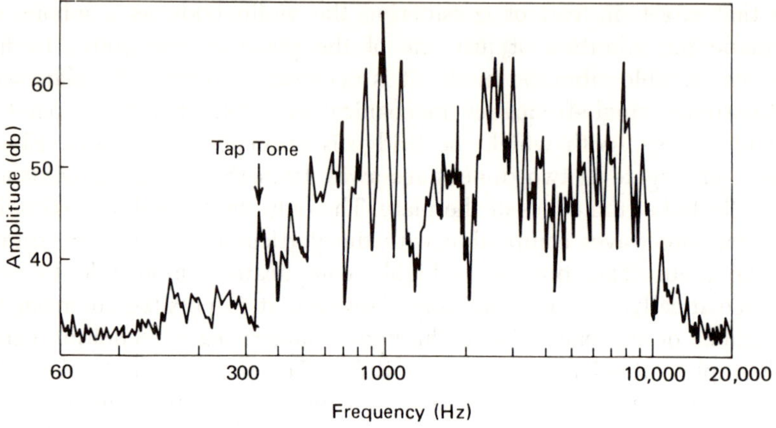

Fig. 4.15. Resonance curve of a violin (Hutchins and Fielding 1968). Permission from *Physics Today* is acknowledged.

of a piano soundboard is even more complicated; this complication, however, ensures a relatively even amplification over a wide range of frequencies.

Fig. 4.15 represents the response curve of a resonator to a single, *harmonic* vibration of given frequency f. What happens if it is excited by a string vibrating with a complex spectrum of harmonics, of frequencies f_1, $f_2 = 2f_1$, $f_3 = 3f_1$, ... etc., and intensities I_1, I_2, I_3, ... ? Each harmonic component will be converted independently, as prescribed by the value of the response function R corresponding to its own frequency. The quality of the resulting sound is thus governed by both, the original string vibration spectrum *and* the response curve of the resonator. It is then quite clear that a resonator will strongly influence the tone quality of the sound of a vibrating string.

As an example, consider the hypothetical spectrum of a vibrating string shown in Fig. 4.16. This string is mounted on a hypothetical soundboard whose response curve is also shown. The output sound spectrum is given in the right graph (relative values). The fundamental is considerably reduced; instead, the fifth harmonic appears enhanced

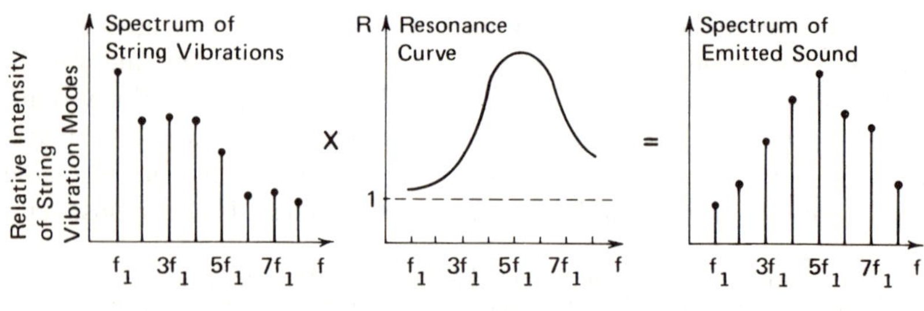

Fig. 4.16

above all others. According to Fig. 4.16, in this example more power would be extracted from the fifth harmonic than from any other. If the string had originally been plucked or struck, this harmonic would decay faster than the others because its energy reservoir would be depleted faster. This leads to a time-dependent change in spectrum or tone quality as the sound dies away. If, on the other hand, the string were to be bowed, the energy loss in each mode would automatically be compensated for by the bowing mechanism, the resulting tone quality remaining constant in time.

An important, but so far little explored subject is the possible existence of a feedback effect of the soundboard on the string's vibration mode frequencies (small shift of fundamental frequency, inharmonicity of upper harmonics) (Schumacher 1972). This effect would be due to the fact that the "fixed" end points of a string, particularly at the bridge in a string instrument, *do* oscillate a tiny bit (page 106). Since this oscillation is coupled to the resonator, the resonance properties of the latter can cause small shifts of the vibration mode frequencies of the string (coupled oscillators).

Finally, we come to a point most important for music. The response curve of a resonator is an inmutable characteristic of a musical instrument. If, for instance, it has a resonance region around, say, 1,000 Hz, it will enhance all upper harmonics whose frequencies fall near 1,000 Hz, no matter *what* note is being sounded (provided, of course, that its fundamental frequency lies below 1,000 Hz) and no matter what the original string vibration spectrum was. A broad resonance region that enhances the upper harmonics lying in a fixed frequency range is called a *formant*. A musical instrument (its resonator) may have several formants. It is believed that formants, i.e., the enhancements of harmonics in certain fixed, characteristic, frequency intervals are used by the auditory system as a most important "signature" of a complex tone in the process of *identification* of a musical instrument (Section 4.8). One of the reasons in favor of this hypothesis is the fact that formants are the only invariable characteristic common to most, if not all, tones of a given instrument, whereas the spectrum of individual tones may vary considerably from one note to another.

4.4 Standing Longitudinal Waves in an Idealized Air Column

Let us consider a long, very thin cylinder, open at both ends (Fig. 4.17). The air inside can be considered as a unidimensional elastic medium (Section 3.2) through which longitudinal waves can propagate. At any point *inside* the cylinder the pressure is allowed to momentarily build up, decrease, or oscillate considerably with respect to the normal atmospheric pressure outside—the rigid walls and the inertia of the remaining air column hold the necessary balance to the forces (3.1) that arise due to the pressure difference. But at the open end points *P* and *Q*, no large pressure variations are allowed even during the shortest interval of time, because nothing is there to balance the arising pressure differences. These points thus must play the role of *pressure nodes,* and any sound wave caused by a perturbation inside the pipe and propagating along it will be reflected at either open end. We hence have a situation formally analogous to the vibrating string, discussed

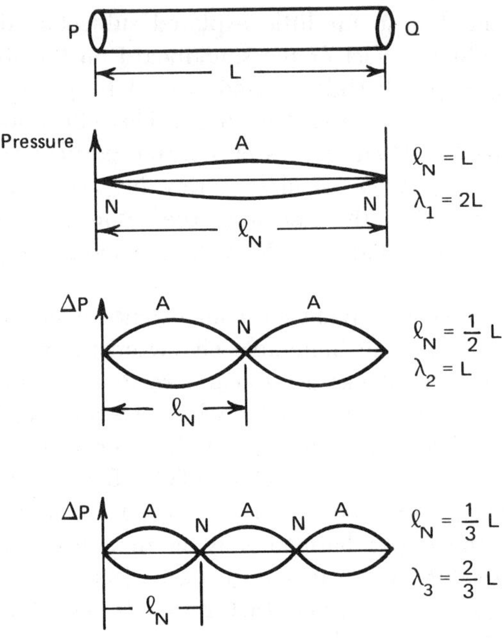

Fig. 4.17. Standing wave modes (pressure variations) in an idealized cylindrical pipe, open at both ends.

in Section 4.1: sound waves generated in the pipe remain trapped inside and *the only possible stable vibration modes are standing longitudinal waves with pressure nodes at the open ends P and Q* (Fig. 4.17). Notice that in view of our discussion in Section 3.3 on page 71, the open end points are *antinodes of displacement,* i.e., points with maximum vibration amplitude.

The open air column does not necessarily have to be physically defined in the manner shown in Fig. 4.17. For instance, there is an open air column comprised between points *P* and *Q* of the pipe shown in Fig. 4.18. Indeed, since there are holes at *P* and *Q*, the air pressure at these points must remain constant and equal to the external pressure. *P* and *Q* thus play the role of open ends of the enclosed air column.

Fig. 4.18 corresponds to the case of an idealized flute, where P is the mouthhole and Q the first open fingerhole.

In a real open pipe of finite diameter, *the pressure nodes do not occur exactly at the open end,* but at a short distance further out ("end correction," p. 120). The relations given below are thus only first approximations.

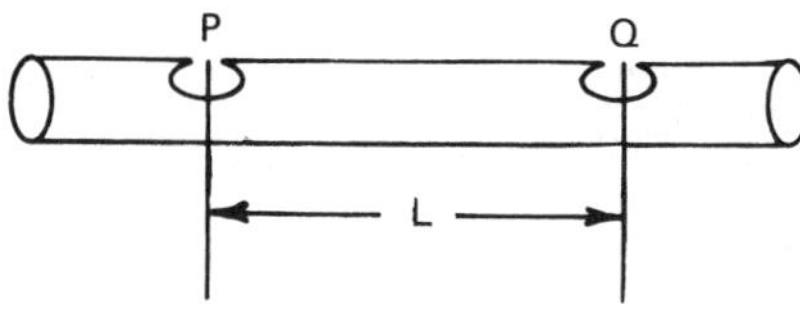

Fig. 4.18

From Fig. 4.17 and relation (3.6) we obtain the frequencies of the vibration modes of an open cylindrical pipe:

$$f_n = \frac{n}{2L}\, 20.1\, \sqrt{t_A} = n f_1 \qquad n = 1, 2, 3, \ldots \tag{4.7}$$

f_1 is the fundamental frequency

$$f_1 = \frac{10.05}{L}\, \sqrt{t_A} \tag{4.8}$$

Remember that t_A is the *absolute* temperature of the air in the pipe, given by (3.5). L in (4.7) and (4.8) must be expressed in *meters.* Taking into account that the wavelength λ_1 of the fundamental tone is related to the length L of the tube by $\lambda_1 = 2L$ (Fig. 4.17) and inspecting Fig. 3.7, one may obtain an idea of typical lengths of open flue organ pipes, flutes, and recorders as a function of frequency. An increase in frequency (pitch) requires a decrease in length. Relation (4.8) also shows the effect of air temperature on the fundamental pitch of a vibrating cylindrical air column. An increase in temperature causes an increase in frequency (sharper tone). Thus flutes and flue organ pipes must be tuned at the temperature at which they are expected to be played. Fortunately, the fundamental frequency (4.8) is controlled by the absolute temperature t_A, appearing under a square root. Both facts make the influence of temperature variations on pitch a rather weak one, but enough to be concerned with—as flautists and organists well know.

We now turn to the case of a narrow cylinder closed at one end (Fig. 4.19). We realize that, whereas at the open end P the pressure must remain constant and equal to that of the outside air (pressure node), at the stopped end Q the inside pressure can build up or decrease without restriction. Indeed, a *pressure antinode* is formed at A. This is more easily understood by considering the actual vibratory motion

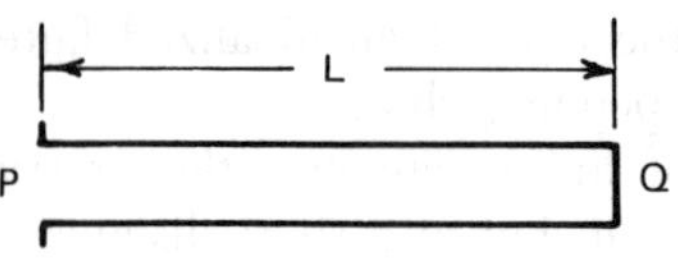

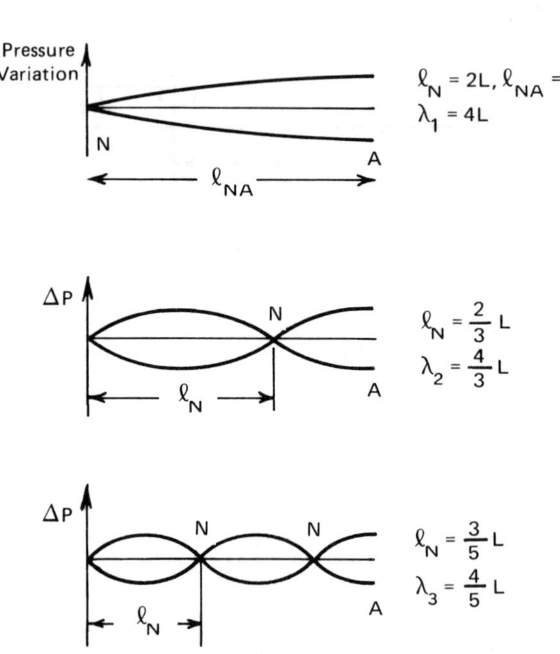

Fig. 4.19. Standing wave mode in an idealized cylindrical pipe, closed at one end.

of the points of the medium. Quite obviously there must be a *vibration node* for all air molecules near Q: they are prevented from longitudinal back-and-forth oscillation by the cover of the pipe. According to the discussion in Section 3.3, such a vibration node corresponds to a pressure antinode.

Fig. 4.19 shows how the standing wave modes "fit" into a stopped pipe in such a way as to always have a pressure node at the open end and a pressure antinode at the stopped end. For the fundamental frequency we find the relation

$$f_1 = \frac{1}{4L}\, 20.1\, \sqrt{t_A} = \frac{5.05}{L}\, \sqrt{t_A} \tag{4.9}$$

[L in meters, t_A absolute temperature (3.5)]. This is exactly *half* of the fundamental frequency (4.8) of an open pipe of the same length. In other words, an idealized stopped cylindrical pipe sounds an octave below the pitch of a similar pipe open at both ends.

With respect to the higher modes of a stopped cylindrical pipe, an inspection of Fig. 4.19 (and conversion of wavelength to frequency) reveals that only *odd* multiples of the fundamental frequency f_1 (4.9) are allowed:

$$f_1, \quad f_3 = 3f_1, \quad f_5 = 5f_1, \ldots \ldots \ldots \tag{4.10}$$

The frequencies $2f_1$, $4f_1$, $6f_1$, ... are forbidden—their modes cannot be stably sustained in an ideally thin stopped cylindrical pipe. In other words, *the overtones of a stopped pipe are odd harmonics of its fundamental.*

The clarinet is perhaps the most familiar example of an instrument behaving very nearly like a stopped cylindrical pipe. The mouthpiece with the reed behaves as the closed end, the bell or the first open fingerhole defining the open end. The fundamental pitch of a note played on the clarinet indeed lies one octave below the note corresponding to the same air column length, played on a flute.

Organs include several stopped pipe ranks. One of the reasons is money and space savings: open bass pipes are very long (according to relation (4.8) an open C_1 pipe is 5.3 m high). The same pipe, if stopped, needs only to be 2.7 m long. Of course, there is more than money at stake: a stopped pipe yields a different quality of sound than an open one of the same fundamental frequency.

Our last case under discussion here is a (very narrow) conical pipe, stopped (closed) at the tip P (Fig. 4.20). The determination of the

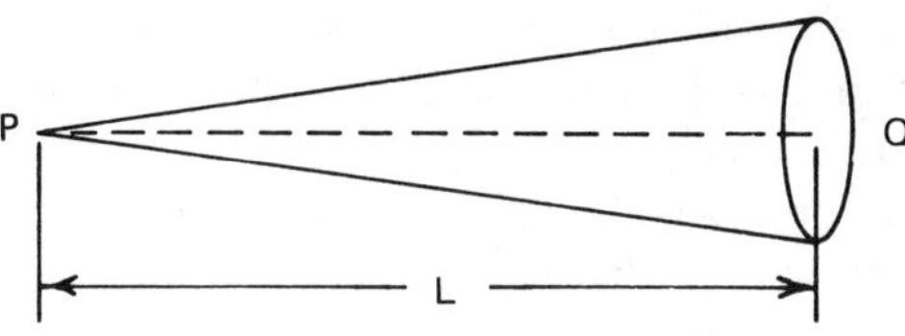

Fig. 4.20

modes of vibration requires a rather complex mathematical analysis. The results can be summarized rather simply: an idealized narrow conical pipe stopped at the tip has the same vibration modes as an open pipe of the same length. In other words, relations (4.7,8) apply. A *truncated* (narrow) cone (Fig. 4.21), closed at the end P, has a series

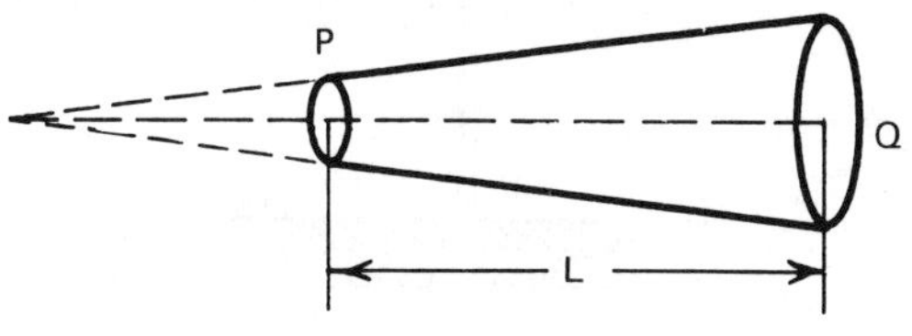

Fig. 4.21

of vibration modes that do not bear the integer number relationship: in the lower frequency range (near the fundamental) they correspond nearly to the modes of an open pipe of the same length L, but for higher frequencies they approach those of a closed cylindrical pipe of length L. In other words, the vibration modes are *inharmonic*.

4.5 Generation of Complex Standing Vibrations in Wind Instruments

The results of the preceding section are idealizations that would become true only for hypothetical air columns (cylinders, cones) of diameters that are very, very small as compared to their length L. This, however, is not the case with real musical instruments and organ pipes. Besides, the air cavities in these instruments are cylindrical or conical only along a certain portion of their length, with more complex shapes near the mouthpiece and the open end (open fingerholes, bells, etc.).

In order to analyze the physical behavior of real wind instruments we must inspect in more detail all phenomena involved. Let us first turn to the *excitation mechanism*. There is no equivalent to the "plucking" or "hitting" of a string in the case of an air column. The reason is that the vibrations of a freely oscillating air column decay almost instantaneously. One may verify this easily by tapping with the hand on one end of an open pipe (the longer the better), or by knocking sharply on its wall, while holding the ear near the other end. A sound burst of pitch equal to the fundamental frequency of the pipe can indeed be heard, but the decay takes place within a fraction of a second. It is thus necessary to have a primary excitation mechanism equivalent to the bowing of a string, that continuously supplies energy to the vibrating air column at a given rate.

There are two distinct types of such mechanisms. The first one consists of a high speed air stream blown against a rigid, sharp edge E (Fig. 4.22), located at a certain distance d exactly above the slit S. This system is aerodynamically unstable: the airstream alternates back

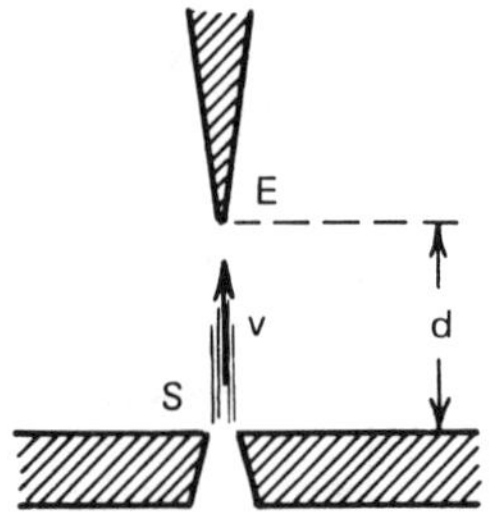

Fig. 4.22

and forth between both sides of the edge, breaking into "rotating puffs" of air called "vortices" or "eddies," which travel upward along both sides of the edge. As the velocity of the stream increases, vortices are created at an increasing rate. Since they represent a periodic perturbation of the ambient air, sound waves are generated when the vortex generation rate falls into the audio domain. The resulting sound is called an *edge tone*.[9] The edge tone mechanism is the primary excitation process for all wind instruments of the flute family and for flue organ pipes. The air stream oscillations are in general complex; for very small flow intensities they become nearly sinusoidal. The fundamental frequency of a free edge tone depends on the air stream velocity v and the distance to the edge d (Fig. 4.22). In the low frequency range it is proportional to the ratio v/d, i.e., it increases with increasing v and decreasing d.

The other excitation mechanism of importance in music is the *reed*, a thin plate made of cane, plastic, or metal, placed in front of a slit of nearly the same shape and of slightly smaller size than the reed (Fig. 4.23). As air is blown into the cavity from below (i.e., the pressure

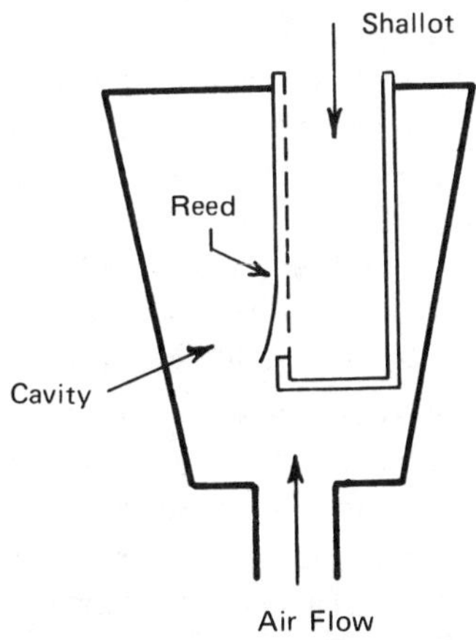

Fig. 4.23

therein is increased), the excess air flows through the small space between the slightly lifted reed and the slit into the shallot. During this flow, the reed is drawn toward the slit.[10] This eventually interrupts the flow; the reed's own elasticity opens the slit again and the whole game starts anew. In other words, the reed starts oscillating back and

---

[9] Vortices are even formed in absence of the edge, provided the slit S is small enough and the velocity v high enough. This represents the basic physics of the *human whistle* where slit size (lip opening) and velocity of the air stream (blowing pressure) determine the fundamental frequency.

[10] By the difference in *dynamic* pressure (not static pressure) on both sides of the reed—the same effect that keeps a flying aircraft aloft!

forth, alternately closing (partially or totally) and opening the slit. The air moves in periodic puffs into the shallot, giving rise to a sound called *reed tone*. The fundamental frequency of a *free* reed tone depends on both the elastic properties of the reed and the excess pressure in the cavity (blowing pressure). In general, the vibratory motion of a free reed is complex, except at very small amplitudes for which it is nearly sinusoidal. Some instruments (oboe, bassoon) have *double reeds*, beating against each other. Also the lips of a brass instrument player can be considered as a (very massive) double reed system.

The edge and reed tones discussed above are seldom used alone ("free" edge and reed tones). In the woodwind instruments they merely serve as the primary excitation mechanism, the energy supplier to the air column in a pipe. In those cases not only the spectrum, but also the frequency of the vibrations of the air stream or the reed are controlled by the air column via a (nonlinear) feedback mechanism. This is accomplished by the sound waves in the air column: the first compressional wave pulse to be produced travels along the pipe, is reflected at the other end (open or closed), and comes back to the mouthpiece (as a rarefaction pulse in open pipes, as a compression pulse in closed ones). There it causes a pressure variation that in the case of woodwinds "overrides" all other forces (aerodynamic or elastic) and thus controls the motion of the air stream or the reed. The resulting pitch is quite different (usually much lower) from that evoked when the corresponding edge or reed tone mechanism is activated freely, in absence of the pipe. This is quite different from the case of a string mounted on a soundboard, whose pitch remains unaffected by the resonator (zero feedback). In the case of brass instruments, the mass of the player's lips is so large that the feedback from the pipe can only influence, but not override, their vibration; the latter must be controlled by the player himself by adjusting the tension of his lips. There are a few musical instruments with open reeds (accordion, harmonica, reed organ).

The tone-buildup process in a wind instrument is very complicated and not yet fully investigated. But it is of capital importance for music. In many instruments, upper harmonics build up faster than the fundamental; sometimes this can be artificially enhanced, giving a characteristic "chiff" to the resulting tone.

To understand the *steady state* sound generation in woodwinds, brasses and organ pipes, it is necessary to analyze the resonance properties of their air columns and the coupling of the latter with the primary excitation mechanism (air stream, reed, or lips). To that effect let us state the following experimentally verified facts: (1) The primary excitation mechanism sustains a periodic oscillation that is complex, of a certain fundamental frequency, and with a series of harmonics of given spectrum. (2) Fundamental frequency and spectrum of the primary oscillation are controlled (influenced, in the case of brass instruments) by the resonance properties of the air column; the total amplitude of the oscillations is determined by the primary energy supply (total air stream flow, blowing pressure). (3) The spectrum of the pressure oscillations outside the instrument (generated sound wave) is related to the internal spectrum by a transformation that is governed by the detailed form and distribution of fingerholes and/or by the shape of the bell.

To explore the resonance properties, i.e., the resonance curve, of the air column in a given wind instrument, one must devise an experimental set-up in analogy to the alternating-current-driven metal string (Section 4.1) or the vibrator-excited violin plate (Section 4.3). This is accomplished by replacing the "natural" excitation mechanism by a mechanical oscillation driver (e.g., an appropriate speaker membrane) and by measuring with a tiny microphone the pressure oscillation amplitudes in the mouthpiece (where a pressure antinode is formed in this setup). The resonance curve is then obtained by plotting the pressure oscillation amplitudes as a function of frequency, for *constant* driver oscillation amplitude. The measured amplitudes are usually expressed in decibels [R in expression (4.6)], referred to some standard level. Curves of this type are also called *input impedance* plots. Fig. 4.24 sketches typical resonance curves obtained for clarinet-type and oboe-type air columns (Benade 1971) (*without* mouthpieces, bells, and open fingerholes). It is important to note that the resonance peaks obtained in this manner correspond to the vibration modes of an air column *closed* at the end of the primary driver, i.e., to a real case in which a *reed* is used as excitation mechanism at one end of the column (pressure antinode, vibration node, at the place of the reed). To find the resonance curve of the same air column corresponding to the case in which it is excited by an air stream (flutes, recorders, organ flue pipes), it is sufficient to plot the negative $-R$ of the values obtained in the previous measurement:[11] resonance peaks become dips and dips become peaks (just turn Fig. 4.24 upside down). The main justification for this procedure is that, in the mouthpiece, the pressure antinode (that appears when a reed is used) is replaced by a *vibration* antinode, i.e., a pressure node, in the case of a flute with an open mouthhole.

Note in Fig. 4.24 that resonance peaks are not at all "sharp"; possible oscillation modes thus do not correspond to unique, discrete frequencies, as it appeared to be in the case of infinitely thin air columns (Section 4.4). Furthermore, in the case of the truncated cone (b), the resonance peaks are asymmetric and inharmonic (see discrepancy from the harmonic multiples $2f_1$, $3f_1$, etc.). Toward high frequencies, the resonance peaks of the truncated cone resemble those of the cylinder. On the other hand, if the cone were complete (till the tip), the resonance

---

[11] Only if R is expressed in *decibels*.

peaks would all lie close to the dips of curve (a) (even harmonics of the cylinder) with very little inharmonicity.

Let us discuss qualitatively how the resonance curve controls the primary excitation mechanism, say, of a reed. For very low intensities (small amplitudes of the reed), its motion is nearly sinusoidal, and, in principle, any resonance peak frequency (Fig. 4.24) could be evoked.

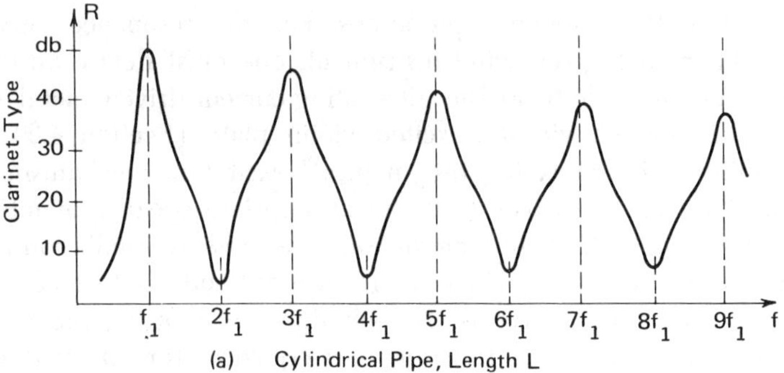

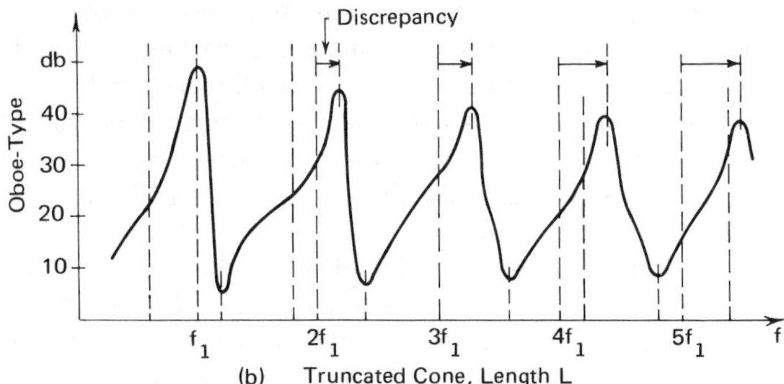

Fig. 4.24. Typical resonance curves (Benade 1971) for clarinet-type (cylindrical) and oboe-type (conical) air columns (without mouthpiece, bell, and open fingerholes).

In practice, however, it is found that only the frequency corresponding to the *tallest* resonance peak is excited at very low intensity level (pianissimo). Usually, this is the peak with the lowest resonance frequency; the evoked sound pertains to the *"low register"* of the instrument.

As the amplitude of the reed oscillation increases (by increasing the blowing pressure), the nonlinear character of the feedback from the air column destroys the harmonic, sinusoidal, vibration of the reed, upper harmonics appear with increasing strength (in general, the intensity of the n-th harmonic grows proportionally to the $2n$-th power of the intensity of the fundamental), and the resulting sound becomes "brighter." At the same time, the fundamental frequency readjusts itself if the upper resonance peaks are somewhat inharmonic. The rule governing this pitch readjustment is the following: the fundamental frequency locks into position in such a way as *to maximize the weighted average height of all resonance values R_1, R_2, R_3, ...*[12] corresponding to the harmonics f_1, $2f_1$, $3f_1$ . . . . . (Benade 1971). If, for instance, the upper resonance peaks deviate from harmonicity as shown in Fig. 4.24b, the pitch of the tone must become sharper as its intensity increases, in order to accommodate the set of increasingly important upper harmonics and place each of them as close as possible to a resonance peak. Due to this effect, a truncated cone will not work as a woodwind unless something is done to minimize the inharmonicity.

An interesting situation arises with the clarinet-type resonance curve (Fig. 4.24a). There, the resonance peaks are situated at only odd integer multiples of the fundamental (see also Section 4.4). Hence, all even harmonic components of the reed oscillation will be strongly attenuated. Starting from a piano-pianissimo in the low register (single-frequency excitation at the fundamental peak) and gradually increasing the blowing pressure will at first tend to evoke the second harmonic. Its energy, however, will be efficiently drained because of the dip at the corresponding frequency (Fig. 4.24a). The resulting increase in loudness (and "brightness") will thus be considerably less for a given increase in blowing pressure than in an oboe-like air column (curve b) where the second harmonic can build up unhindered. This is why transitions from *ppp* to *pp* are more easily managed in a clarinet than in an oboe or saxophone.

Finally, another noteworthy fact in Fig. 4.24 is the almost identical location of the *dips* in both curves. When these dips are converted into peaks by plotting $-R$ instead of R to obtain the resonance curve of these air columns when they are excited with an air stream (open mouthhole), one obtains a practically identical harmonic series in both examples. Consequently, cylinder and truncated cone can be used almost indistinctly to make flute-type instruments.

So far we have considered standing waves in which the fundamental frequency is determined by the first (lowest frequency) peak of the resonance curve, yielding the low register tones of a woodwind instrument. In the *"middle register,"* the fundamental frequency lies close to the second resonance peak. In reed instruments this is realized by decreasing the size of the first resonance peak below that of the second and by shifting its position away from the harmonic series. The register hole or speaker hole accomplishes this function. In the flute, this transition, or *"overblow,"* is accomplished by means of a change (increase)

---

[12] Weighted with the corresponding spectral intensity values I_1, I_2, I_3, ...

of the air speed blown against the wedge. Notice that in the first over-blow of a clarinet-type reed the pitch jumps to the third harmonic or *twelfth* (second peak, Fig. 4.24a), whereas cylindrical-bore reeds (and all flutes) have their first overblow on the *octave* (second harmonic, Fig. 4.24b).

Another overblow leads to the *top register* of the woodwinds, with fundamental frequencies based on the third and/or fourth resonance peaks. To accomplish this with a reed instrument, the first two resonance peaks must be depressed and shifted in frequency to destroy the har-monic relationship.

Organ pipes work on essentially the same principles as a flute (flue pipes, open and stopped) or as a reed woodwind (reed pipes). The main difference is that since there is one pipe for each note for a given stop, tone holes and overblowing are unnecessary. Organ pipes are al-ways operated in the low register (with a few exceptions in "romantic" organs). Resonance curves of open flue organ pipes have peaks located near the integer multiples of the fundamental frequency, with a slight inharmonicity which depends on the ratio $r = $ diameter/length. Stopped pipe resonance curves resemble that of the upper graph in Fig. 4.24 with maxima at odd multiples of the fundamental. The fundamental frequency is slightly misplaced with respect to the value given by rela-tion 4.8 (open pipe) or 4.9 (stopped pipe). These relations, however, may still be used if a correction of value $0.3 \times$ diameter is added, for each open end, to the length L ("end correction"). Reed organ pipes range from the type in which the reed vibration is strongly controlled by the feedback from the air column (e.g., trumpet-family stops) to a type in which the reed vibration is practically autonomous (regal-family stops).

4.6   Sound Spectra of Wind Instrument Tones

Resonance characteristic of the air column and excitation mechanism collaborate to determine the spectrum and the intensity of the standing wave in the bore of the instrument. Fig. 4.24 showed two hypothetical resonance curves; real instruments, however, display a more complicated behavior due to the peculiar shape of the mouthpiece (and mouthpipe), the shape and distribution of open fingerholes, the effect of the bell, and, in the case of flutes, the effect of air speed on the width and position of the resonance peaks (Benade 1971). Here we can only sum-marize briefly the most important effects. The *fingerholes*, besides of course determining the effective length of the air column and, hence, the absolute position of the resonance peaks, are partly responsible for a *cut-off* of the resonance peaks above about 1,500–2,000 Hz. This cutoff has an important effect on timbre (attenuation of high harmonics) and on the dynamic control of loud woodwind tones, particularly in the middle and high registers. In the oboe, the reed cavity and the constriction in the staple contribute to decrease the inharmonicity of the truncated cone resonances.

The brasses deserve special attention in this section. As already pointed out, the feedback mechanism is less efficient in the determination of the fundamental frequency, and the player must set the buzzing frequency of his lips near to the wanted frequency in order to elicit the right pitch. In a brass instrument the upper harmonics are created by the oscillating resonance properties of the mouthpiece caused by the alternate opening and closing of the lips (Backus and Hundley 1971) rather than by a feed-back-controlled nonsinusoidal motion of the latter. Mouthpiece, tapered mouthpipe, main cylindrical bore, and bell combine in such a way as to yield a characteristic resonance curve rather different from that of a typical woodwind. Fig. 4.25 gives an ex-

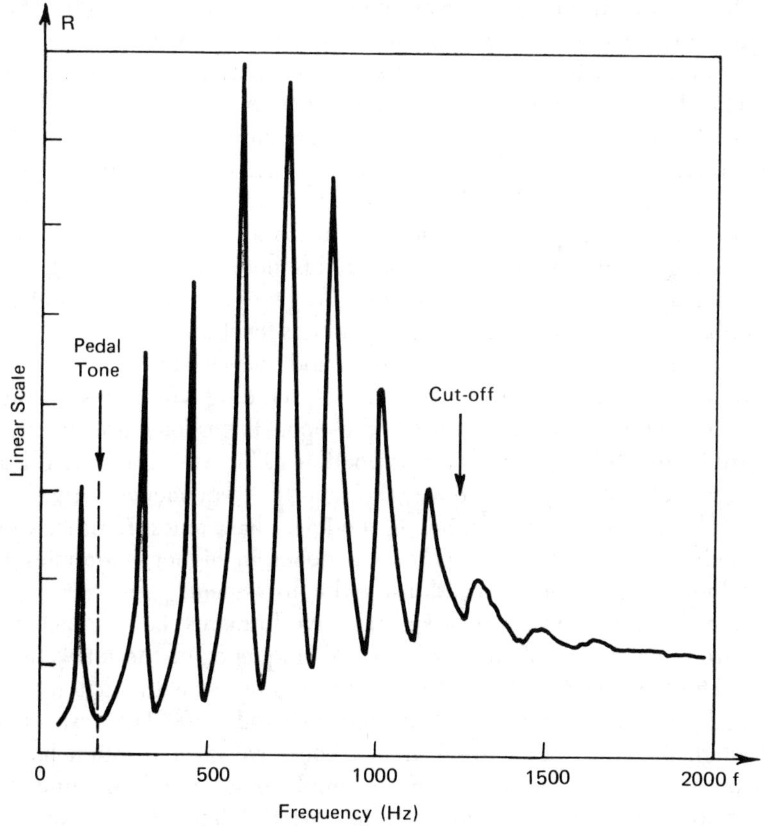

Fig. 4.25. Resonance curve of a trumpet (Benade 1971) (given in linear scale). By permission of Prof. A. Benade, Case Western Reserve University, Ohio.

ample (Benade 1971). Notice the marked cut-off frequency (mainly determined by the bell) and the large hump of peaks and dips in the mid-frequency range (mainly governed by the shape of the mouthpiece). This hump plays a crucial role in shaping the tone quality of brass instruments. Finally, the first resonance peak lies *below* the fundamental frequency (marked by the arrow) corresponding to the rest of the peaks. Notice also the characteristic asymmetry of the peaks in the low frequency range (similar to those of a truncated cone, Fig. 4.24b), as compared to the high frequency region (where their shape is inverted).

Brasses do not have tone holes to alter the effective length of their air columns—changes in pitch are mainly effected by overblowing, i.e., making the fundamental frequency jump from one resonance peak to another. This is accomplished by appropriately adjusting the lip tension. Up to the 8th harmonic can be reached in the trumpet, and the 16th harmonic in the French horn. To obtain notes between resonance peaks, a system of valves offers a limited choice of slightly different pipe lengths. In the trombone, a continuous change of tube length (hence of pitch) is possible through the slide. Since the lowest resonance peak is out of tune with the rest of the almost harmonic series of peaks, it cannot be used. Rather, the fundamental frequency of the lip vibration is set at the value of the *missing* fundamental (arrow in Fig. 4.25) that corresponds to the second, third, etc. peaks. This leads to the so-called *"pedal note"* of a brass instrument (used only in the trombone). Obviously, the fundamental tracking mechanism (Section 2.7) is put into action in the pitch perception of this note. Since the higher harmonics must be definitely present for the generation of the pedal note, it can be played only at considerable loudness levels.

The spectral composition of the sound waves emitted by a wind instrument is different from that of the standing vibrations sustained in its air column. The bell and/or the open fingerholes are mainly responsible for this spectral transformation. This transformation leaves the spectral composition above the cut-off frequency relatively unchanged, while it tends to attenuate the lower harmonics. In other words, woodwind and brass tone spectra are richer in higher harmonics than the vibrations actually produced inside the instrument.

Some wind instrument tone spectra have formants, i.e., characteristics that are independent of the fundamental frequency of the tone (Section 4.3). The bassoon and English horn are examples, with (not too well-defined) spectral enhancement around 450 and 1,100 Hz, respectively. Although not an explicit topic in this book, we must mention here the *human voice* as the most notable example of a "wind instrument" in which formants play a crucial role: they are the determining characteristic of all *vowel sounds*. Formants in the human voice are mainly determined by the resonance properties of the nasofaringeal cavity (Flanagan 1972). The shape of this cavity determines which of two main frequency ranges of the vocal chord vibrations are to be enhanced. These, in turn, determine whether the outcoming sound is "ah," "ee," "oh," etc.

4.7   Trapping and Absorption of Sound Waves in a Closed Environment

Musical instruments are usually played in rooms, halls, auditoriums, and churches. The sound a listener perceives under these conditions is not at all identical to the one emitted by the instrument. For this reason, the enclosure in which an instrument is played may be considered a natural extension of the latter, with the difference that whereas a given musical instrument has certain immutable acoustical properties, those of the enclosure may vary widely from case to case and from place to place. The subject of auditorium acoustics is as important for music as is the physics of musical instruments.

To analyze the effect of an enclosure on a musical sound source placed somewhere inside, let us consider a musical instrument at position S and a listener at position L (which may coincide with S if the listener is the player) in a room of perfectly reflecting walls (Fig. 4.26). The

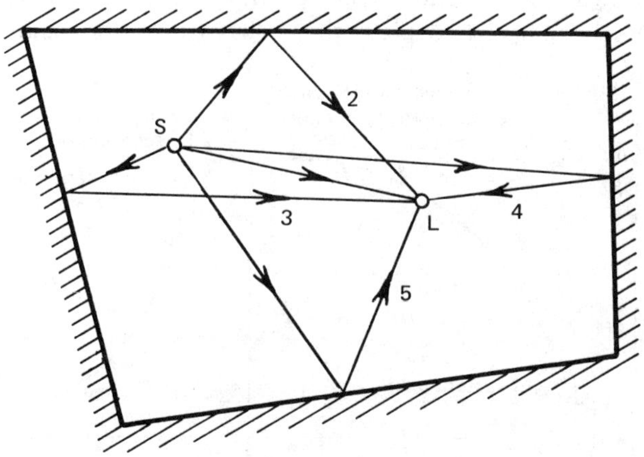

Fig. 4.26.

instrument starts playing a given note at time $t = 0$, holding its intensity steady afterwards. We assume that the sound is emitted equally into all directions. As sound waves propagate away from S, the listener will receive a first signal after the short interval of time SL/V which it takes the *direct* sound to travel from S to L [for instance, if $SL = 10$ m, $V = 334$ m/sec (relation 3.6), the time of direct arrival is 0.3 sec; for the player it is practically zero]. As we shall see in Section 5.1, the direct sound plays a key role in the perceptual process. Immediately thereafter, reflected waves (trajectories 2, 3, 4, 5, etc.) will pass through point L in rapid succession (in the figure, the reflections on the floor and the ceiling have been ignored). The first few reflections, if very pronounced and well separated from each other, are called echoes. This game continues with secondary, tertiary, and multiple reflections (not shown in the figure). As time goes on, and the instrument keeps sounding, acoustical energy passing through point L will keep building up. If there were no absorption at all, the sound waves would "fill" the room traveling in all directions and the acoustical energy emitted by the instrument would accumulate and remain trapped in the enclosure; the loudness would thus build up gradually at any point inside.[13] In the real case, of course, there is absorption every time a sound wave is reflected. Hence, the sound wave intensity will not increase indefinitely but level off when the power dissipated in the absorption processes has become equal to the rate at which energy is fed in by the source (a similar situation to the vibration build-up in a bowed string, Fig. 4.10). This "equilibrium" intensity level I_m of the diffuse sound is much higher than that of the direct sound (except in the neighborhood of the sound source).

When the sound source is shut off, an inverse process develops: first, the direct sound disappears, then the first, second, etc. reflections. Fig. 4.27 schematically depicts the behavior of the sound intensity

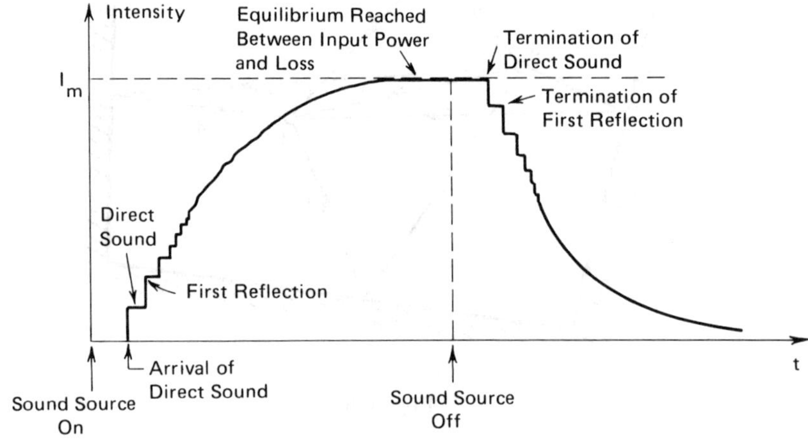

Fig. 4.27. Typical tone intensity buildup and decay in a hall (linear scale).

at a given point in a typical enclosure. The sound decay, after the source has been shut off, is called *reverberation* and represents an effect

---

[13] For almost any kind of shapes of rooms and positions of the source therein, there may be regions practically inaccessible to sound waves emitted from S ("blind" spots), or regions into which sound waves are focussed (e.g., the focal points in elliptic enclosures).

124

of greatest importance in room acoustics. This decay is nearly exponential (e.g., see Fig. 4.8); quite arbitrarily one defines *reverberation time* as the interval it takes the sound level to decrease by 60 db. According to Table 3.2 this represents an intensity decrease by a factor of 1 million. Desirable reverberation times in good medium-sized concert halls are of the order of 1.5–2 seconds. Longer times would blurr too much typical tone successions; shorter times would make the music sound "dry" and dull (see Section 4.8).

We may discuss a few simple mathematical relationships that appear in room acoustics. Let us imagine an enclosure of perfectly reflecting walls with no absorption whatsoever, but with a built-in *hole* of area A. Whenever the maximum intensity I_m is reached (Fig. 4.27), acoustical energy will be escaping through the hole at a rate given by the product $I_m A$.[14] Since this corresponds to the steady state in which the power P supplied by the instrument equals the energy loss rate, we can set $P = I_m A$, or

$$I_m = \frac{P}{A} \tag{4.11}$$

In a real case, of course, we do not have perfectly reflecting walls with holes in them. However, we still may *imagine* a real absorbing wall as if it were made of a perfectly reflecting material with holes in it, the latter representing a fraction a of its total surface. a is called the absorption coefficient of the wall's material. A surface of S square meters, of absorption coefficient a, has the same absorption properties as a perfectly reflecting wall of the same size but with a hole of area $A = Sa$. Absorption coefficients depend on the frequency of the sound (usually increasing for higher frequencies), and have values that range from 0.01 (marble; an almost perfect reflector) to as much as 0.9 (acoustical tiles). Taking all this into account, we can rewrite relation (4.11) in terms of the actual wall surfaces S_1, S_2, ... with corresponding absorption coefficients a_1, a_2, ... :

$$I_m = \frac{P}{S_1 a_1 + S_2 a_2 + \cdots} \tag{4.12}$$

This relation can be used to estimate auditorium sizes needed to achieve wanted values of I_m, for a given instrument power P, and a given distribution of absorbing wall materials.

The reverberation time τ_r is found to be proportional to the volume V of the hall and inversely proportional to the absorbing area of the walls $A = S_1 a_1 + S_2 a_2 + \cdots$. Experiments show that, approximately,

$$\tau_r = 0.16 \frac{V}{S_1 a_1 + S_2 a_2 + \cdots} \tag{4.13}$$

---

[14] It is assumed here that I_m represents the diffuse, *omni*directional, sound energy flow.

with V in cubic meters, S in square meters, τ_r in seconds. Since the absorption coefficients usually increase with sound frequency, τ_r will decrease with increasing pitch: bass notes reverberate longer than treble notes.

One of the problems in room acoustics is that the *audience* influences greatly (increases) the absorption properties of a hall. This must be taken into account in the design of auditoriums. In order to minimize the effects related to the unpredictable size of an audience and its spatial distribution, it would be necessary to build a seat whose absorption coefficient is nearly independent of whether it is occupied or not. The absorbing effect of the audience is maximally felt in enclosures with very long reverberation times, such as in churches and cathedrals. No single performer is so exposed to (and harassed by) a changing acoustical environment as an organist.

Tone distribution, build-up and decay, as well as the frequency-dependence of the absorption coefficients, have a profound effect on the physical characteristics of musical tones emitted by an instrument in a real environment, hence on the perception of music by the listener. The time dependence of tones is deeply affected: transient characteristics are altered, and, for instance, a staccato note becomes stretched in time depending on the reverberation properties of the hall. The tone spectrum is also affected, since the absorption coefficients are all frequency dependent. Finally, taking into account that the phases of the waves passing through a given point in a field of reverberant sound are randomly mixed, it can be shown that the resulting SPL of each harmonic component will also fluctuate at random, introducing a limit to the listener's ability to recognize tone quality in a closed musical environment (Plomp and Steeneken 1972).

There are other second-order effects, usually neglected, related to a wave phenomenon called *diffraction*. When a sound wave hits an obstacle (e.g., a pillar in a church or a person sitting in front of the listener) three situations may arise: (1) If the wavelength of the sound wave is much smaller than the size (diameter) of the obstacle (e.g., a high-pitch tone) (Fig. 4.28a), a sound "shadow" will be formed behind the obstacle, with "normal" reflection occurring on the front side. (2) If

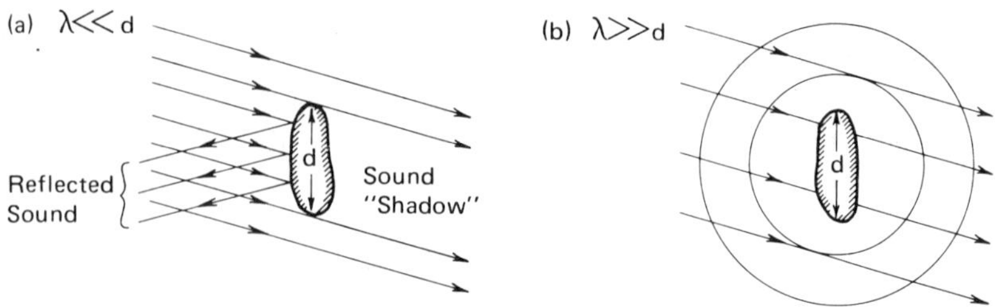

Fig. 4.28

126

both, obstacle and wavelength are of roughly the same magnitude, a more complicated situation arises, in which the obstacle itself acts as a sound reemitter, radiating into all directions (not shown in Fig. 4.28). (3) If the wavelength is much larger than the obstacle (Fig. 4.28b) (e.g., bass tones), the latter will not disturb the sound wave at all, which will propagate almost undisturbed. Regular arrangements of obstacles (as the distribution of seats or people in the audience) may lead to interference patterns for given wavelengths and directions of propagation. Finally, standing waves may build up for certain configurations of the enclosure, certain frequencies, and certain positions of the source. This leads to the formation of annoying nodes and antinodes (Section 3.3) in the room.

4.8   Perception of Tone Quality

Whereas considerable research has been done on the perception of pitch and loudness of pure tones (Sections 2.3, 8; 3.4, 5), much remains to be done in the study of the perception of quality or timbre of complex tones. That the quality of a tone can be modified by reinforcing certain overtones has been known for many centuries. Indeed, genuine *tone synthesis* was first performed by pipe organ builders in the 13th or 14th century. Organs of those times did not have multiple stops; rather, each key sounded a fixed number of pipes called "Blockwerk," composed of one or several pipes tuned to the fundamental pitch of the written note, plus a series of pipes respectively tuned to the octave, the twelfth, the fifteenth, etc., following the series of upper harmonics (excluding the seventh). The particular combination of loudness chosen for each component pipe determined the particular quality of sound of the instrument. Later on, the first multiple stops appeared: they allowed the organist to selectively turn on or off the various ranks of pipes corresponding to the upper harmonics in the "Blockwerk," and thus choose from among several options the particular quality of sound of the organ (and alter the loudness—Section 3.4). It was only one or two centuries later that new independent stops were added, in the form of ranks of pipes of individually different quality of sound.

Synthesis of sound is thus rather old hat. However, *analysis* of sound, i.e., the individualization of upper harmonics that appear simultaneously in a naturally produced tone, was not explicitly mentioned in the literature until 1636, when the remarkable French scientist-philosopher-musician, Père Mersenne published the first study of the (qualitative) analysis of the upper harmonics present in a complex tone.

Two main questions arise regarding perception of timbre: (1) why does a complex tone, made up of a superposition of different frequencies, give rise to only *one* pitch sensation; (2) what is it that enables us to distinguish one tone spectrum from another, even if pitch and loudness are the same? To attempt to find an answer to these questions, let us analyze the auditory detection and perception process step by step, this time for a *complex* sound wave impinging on the eardrum. The eardrum will move in and out periodically with a vibration pattern dictated by the complex, nonsinusoidal vibration pattern of the wave. This motion is transmitted mechanically by the chain of ossicles to the oval window membrane, which reproduces exactly the same complex vibration pattern. Neither eardrum nor bone chain "know" that the vibration they are transmitting is made up of a superposition of different harmonics. This analysis is only done in the next step.

The complex vibration of the oval window membrane triggers traveling waves in the cochlear fluid. This is the stage at which the separation into different frequency components takes place. As stated in Section 2.3, the resonance region for a given frequency component (region of the basilar membrane where the traveling wave causes maximum excitation) is located at a position that depends on frequency. A complex tone will thus give rise to a whole multiplicity of resonance regions (Fig. 4.29), one for each harmonic, whose actual positions can be ob-

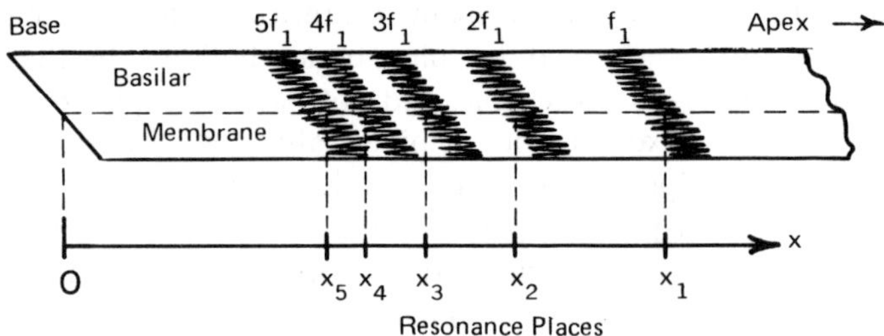

Fig. 4.29

tained with the aid of Fig. 2.8. In view of the near-logarithmic relationship between x and f, the resonance regions will crowd closer and closer together as one moves up the harmonic series (Fig. 4.29). Since each resonance region is not "sharp" but extended over a certain length (Section 2.4), overlap between neighboring resonance regions will occur, particularly for higher harmonics. Actually, beyond about the sixth harmonic, all resonance regions overlap, lying within a critical band, and it makes little sense to consider them individually.[15] Each one of the resonance regions of the basilar membrane oscillates with its own reso-

---

[15] Experiments have indeed shown that for usual musical instruments, due to this overlap (frequency discrimination, Section 2.4), harmonics beyond about the seventh cannot be heard out (Plomp 1964).

128

nance frequency and with a phase that is related (but not equal) to the phase of the corresponding harmonic (Fourier component) in the original eardrum oscillation (Flanagan 1972). Overlapping, of course, complicates this picture considerably.

A single complex tone thus elicits an extremely complicated situation in the cochlea. Why then do we really perceive this tone as *one* entity, of well-defined pitch, loudness, and quality? This seems to be due to the one feature which these multiple resonance regions have in common: as stated in Section 2.7, *pairs of consecutive components of a harmonic series yield one common repetition rate*—that of the fundamental. When listening to a complex tone, *our auditory system pays more attention to the output of the periodicity pitch mechanism* (which yields *one* unique pitch sensation) *than to the primary pitch of the individual harmonic components*. If we want to "hear out" the first six or seven upper harmonics of a steadily sounding complex tone, we must command a "turn-off" (inhibition) of the dominating periodicity pitch mechanism and focus our attention on the initially choked output from the more primitive primary pitch mechanism, determined by the spatial position of the activated regions of the basilar membrane (Section 2.3). This inhibiting and refocusing takes a considerable time—considerably longer than the buildup of the general tone-processing mechanism (Section 3.5).[1] This is why upper harmonics cannot be heard out in short tones, or rapidly decaying tones[16]. Periodicity pitch or fundamental tracking (Section 2.7) thus is the psychophysical mechanism that helps to tie together into one sensation the complicated distribution of activity along the basilar membrane evoked by a complex tone. The total rate of neural pulses reaching the brain very likely yields the corresponding loudness sensation (Section 3.5).

With respect to the perception of *tone quality* or *timbre*, we must make a clear distinction between the static situation that arises when we listen to a steady complex tone of constant fundamental frequency, intensity, and spectrum, and the more realistic dynamic situation when a complex tone with transient characteristics is perceived as part of a musically relevant context. Let us first analyze the static case. Psychoacoustical experiments with electronically generated steady complex tones, of equal pitch and loudness but different spectra and phase relationships among the harmonics, show that the timbre sensation is mainly controlled by the spectrum (Plomp 1970). Phase changes, although clearly perceptible, particularly when effected among the high frequency components, play only a secondary role. The *static* sensation of quality or *timbre thus emerges as the perceptual correlate of the activity dis-*

---

[16] The fact that the seventh harmonic is a dissonance has been worrying musicians for a long time. This worry is unfounded, though. The seventh harmonic is extremely difficult to be singled out, even in steady, electronically generated complex tones (Plomp 1964).

tribution evoked along the basilar membrane—provided that a common repetition rate is present to bind everything into a "single-tone" sensation. By dividing the audible frequency range into bands of about ⅓ octave each (roughly corresponding to a critical band, Section 2.4), and by measuring the intensity or sound energy flow that for a given complex tone is contained in each band, it was possible to define quantitative "dissimilarity indices" for the (steady) sounds of various musical instruments, which correlate well with psychophysically determined timbre similarity and dissimilarity judgments (Plomp and Steeneken 1971). It is important to point out that the timbre sensation is controlled by the *absolute* distribution of sound energy in the critical bands, not by the intensity values relative to that of the fundamental. This is easily verified by listening to a record or magnetic tape played at the wrong speed. This procedure leaves relative spectra unchanged, merely shifting all frequencies up or down; yet a clear change in timbre of all instruments is perceived.

The static timbre sensation is a "multidimensional" psychological magnitude related not to one but to a whole set of physical parameters of the original acoustical stimulus (the set of intensities in all critical bands).[17] This is the main reason semantic descriptions of tone quality are more difficult to make than those of the "unidimensional" pitch and loudness. Except for the broad denominations ranging from "dull" or "stuffy" (few upper harmonics), to "nasal" (mainly odd harmonics), to "bright" or "sharp" (many enhanced upper harmonics), most of the qualifications given by musicians invoke a comparison with instrumental tones ("flutey," "stringy," "reedy," "brassy," "organ-tone-like," etc.).

Here we come to the more realistic dynamic situation. Our subjective reaction to complex tones depends quite appreciably on the *context* of which they are a part (Houtsma and Goldstein 1971). The performance of tasks that are musically "meaningful" such as the identification of the tone source, i.e., the instrument, and the recognition of melodies or harmonies greatly influences how complex tones are processed in the brain. This applies even to the pitch perception: Experiments with electronically generated spectral components convincingly showed that the attachment of a single pitch to complex sounds is greatly facilitated by, or sometimes even requires, the presentation of the test tones in the form of a "meaningful" melody (Houtsma and Goldstein 1971). Individual electronically synthesized complex tones, taken out of a musical context, may often lead to ambiguous or multiple pitch sensations.

---

[17] Although there are about 15 critical bands in the musically relevant frequency range whose intensities ought to be specified in order to determine the spectrum, a study on vowel identification (Klein, Plomp, and Pols 1970) indicates that only *four* independent intensity parameters (each one a specific linear combination of the intensities in all critical bands) are sufficient to specify a complex tone within the auditory system's "timbre resolution capability."

4.9 Recognition of Musical Sounds

Timbre perception is, indeed, just a first stage of the operation of tone source *recognition*—in music, the identification of the instrument. From this point of view, tone quality perception is the mechanism by means of which information is extracted from the auditory signal in such a way as to make it suitable for: (1) *storage* in the memory *with an adequate label of identification*, and (2) *comparison* with previously stored and identified information. The first operation involves *learning* or conditioning. A child who learns to recognize a given musical instrument is presented repeatedly with a melody played on that instrument and told: "This is a clarinet." His brain extracts suitable information from the succession of auditory stimuli, labels this information with the qualification "clarinet" and stores it in the memory. The second operation represents the conditioned response to a learned pattern: When the child hears a clarinet play after the learning experience, his brain compares the information extracted from the incoming signal (i.e., the tone quality) with stored cues, and, if a successful match is found, conveys the response: "a clarinet." On the other hand, if we listen to a "new" sound, e.g., a series of tones concocted with an electronic synthesizer, our information-extracting system will feed the cues into the matching mechanism, which will then try desperately to compare the input with previously stored information. If this matching process is unsuccessful, a new storage "file" will eventually be opened up for this new, now identified, sound quality. If the process is only partly successful, we react with such judgments as: "almost like a clarinet" or "like a barking trombone."

What are the neural processes that lead to quality perception and tone source identification? Few details are known in this field, and we can only sketch some of the current ideas. First, we note that experiments have shown that neurons in the cortical areas to which the afferent transmission system from a sensorial organ is wired, are *"feature-detectors,"* responding to well-defined but complex physical features of the original sensorial stimulus. In the visual cortex, for instance, neurons have been found that respond only to dark or light bars or edges in a given part of the visual field, inclined with a certain angle, or to a line moving in a certain fashion (Hubel 1971). In the auditory cortex, too, there are neurons that seem to respond only to certain types of complex sounds (Simmons 1970). This exogenous, externally stimulated activity of a cortical neuron is the result of neural signal processing in the afferent pathway from the sensor to the cortex, controlled by the particular way these afferent neurons are wired and interact with each other. A static complex sound of given harmonic spectrum probably elicits a well-defined firing pattern in a well-defined distribution of cortical neurons, and we report a given sensation of timbre. We must point out that this is very likely a *collective* phenomenon involving large ensembles of neurons; there is experimental evidence showing that, in general, one isolated neuron responds to many different kinds of input characteristics (Gerstein and Kiang 1964), thus cooperating in the detection of a large variety of input features. It is the distribution in time and space of neural activity that seems to be locked unambiguously to a given stimulus feature (in our case, a given musical sound). In more physical terms, neural response in the brain cortex represents a (four-dimensional) "holographic" image of the stimuli, in which information on one "point" (or feature) of the input is spread in space and time over a large number of "points" (or neurons) of the cortex.

When neural activity is displayed on the cortex, we report a given sensation. However, experiments have shown that *the cortical activity evoked by a given stimulus is profoundly altered if the information carried by that stimulus has a certain meaning* (John 1972). To the peripherally triggered firing pattern, an endogenous activity or *readout signal* is added (with a typical delay of 50–80 milliseconds), triggered internally in the brain by higher order operations of comparison and identification, somehow representing the conscient experience related to the act of perception. This readout signal is found as a common, coherent pattern of activity spread over many different areas of the brain. It is absent altogether if the original signal is meaningless (i.e., not related to previously stored or learned messages) or if no attention[18] is being paid to the stimulus. Experiments with animals have shown that a readout signal may sometimes be in error, i.e., may not correspond to the externally evoked activity—in those cases the behavioral conditioned response also comes out in error!

It is believed that the replay of a given endogenous readout pattern represents the elementary act of *remembering*. When this pattern is triggered externally while we listen to a tone, we "remember" that this tone comes, say, from a clarinet. When this activity is released internally (by some association or by a volitive command), we are remembering the sound of a clarinet in *absence* of a true external sound. This then represents the most simple form of activation of the "internal hearing mechanism." Experiments with vision have shown that, for instance, the mere imagination of a geometrical form evokes activity in the visual cortex very similar to that externally evoked when the subject actually sees that form (Herrington and Schneidau 1968). A similar effect is likely to occur with the imagination of musical tones and musical forms.

Nothing is known as yet on how the readout activity is actually produced. Obviously, it must involve a complex interaction between different centers of the brain. When we listen to a "new" musical instru-

---

[18] "Attention" probably means to let a given readout pattern of neural activity spread over a large area of the brain by willfully inhibiting all other potential sources of readout patterns.

ment and at the same time are told what the instrument is, the primary exogenous auditory cortical activity evoked by the musical sound and the activity in other centers elicited by the awareness of the name or physical appearance of the instrument, interact somehow in the interconnecting neural tissue, giving rise to the formation of a readout pattern that is a signature of that particular experience. During the initial phase of learning, this readout pattern can be triggered only by the *simultaneous concurrence* of the different inputs that are part of the learning experience (e.g., the instrument's sound and the instrument's appearance). As a result of repetitive stimulation, however, some long lasting alterations occur in the intervening neural tissue (probably in the form of changes in synaptic threshold values of the activated neurons). These alterations are such that, in the future, the same readout patterns can be elicited even if *only one* of the originally concurrent input forms appears. Thus, if we hear tones from a "known" instrument, the activation of the corresponding readout pattern tells us what instrument it is. On the other hand, the same read out pattern can be triggered from the "other end" by "thinking" about the instrument—and the spread of this activity onto the auditory cortex will allow us to "hear" its tones internally.

One school of thought believes that the alterations appear in physically well-defined and localized pathways of enhanced neural conductivity, called neural *engrams* (Eccles 1970). This capacity of "self-organization" is believed to represent the most fundamental property of the cortical and subcortical neural networks. Experiments conducted to study the effects of ablations of cerebral tissue on memory and on recognition operations point against the existence of a highly localized "seat" of memory (John 1972). Current thought is that temporal relations between firing patterns averaged over a large ensemble of brain cells are more significant than a localized spatial distribution of this activity and the actual firing pattern of a reduced number of specific neurons. Learning, according to this view, is to increase the probability of recurrence of a given coherent firing pattern in the neural network—that one triggered by the particular constellation of multiple input repeatedly experienced during the learning process. In other words, learning is not represented so much by an increase of the storage of information *per se,* but by appropriate modifications of the information-processing *mechanisms,* and memory emerges in this picture as the storage of information-processing *instructions,* rather than as the storage of information on facts (features).

We have presented the perception of tone quality as being the first step of an identification mechanism—that of the instrument to which the tone belongs. Musicians will protest and say that there is far more to the sensation of timbre than merely providing cues to find out "what is playing." For instance, what is it that makes one instrument sound more "beautiful" than another of the same kind? First we should point out that this is obviously related to a further degree of sophistication of the identification mechanism mentioned above: we can learn to extract an increasingly refined amount of information from the sound vibration patterns of an instrument, so as to be able to distinguish among different samples of instruments of the same kind. *Why* some vibration patterns appear more "beautiful" than others is not known. A great deal of research (good and bad) has been attempted, for instance, to find out what physical characteristics make a Stradivarius violin a great instrument. Many of these characteristics are dynamic in character, and most of them seem more related to the major or minor facility with which the *player* can control the wanted tone "color" (timbre), than to a "passive" effect on a listener. To a large extent the impression on the listener is based on learned experience: we have been *told* since the inception of our musical training which tones are to be labeled as beautiful, and which not! And our brain has learned to build up the corresponding identifying readout patterns, based on a tremendously refined information-processing of the incoming acoustical signal.

References

Backus, J., and T. C. Hundley. 1971. Harmonic generation in the trumpet. *J. Acoust. Soc. Am.* **49**:509.

Benade, A. H. 1971. Physics of wind instrument tone and response. American Association for the Advancement of Science, Symposium on Sound and Music, December.

Culver, C. A. 1956. *Musical Acoustics.* McGraw Hill Book Company, New York.

Eccles, J. C. 1970. *Facing Reality.* Springer-Verlag, New York.

Flanagan, J. L. 1972. *Speech Analysis, Synthesis and Perception.* 2nd ed. Springer-Verlag, New York.

Friedlander, F. G. 1953. On the oscillations of a bowed string. *Cambridge Phil. Soc. Proc.* **49**:516.

Gerstein, G. L., and N. Kiang. 1964. *Exp. Neurol.* **10**:1.

Herrington, R. N., and P. Schneidau. 1968. *Experientia* **24**:1136.

Houtsma, A. J. M., and J. L. Goldstein. 1971. Perception of musical intervals: evidence for the central origin of the pitch of complex tones. Massachusetts Institute of Technology, Research Laboratory of Electronics, Technical Report 484; 1972. *J. Acoust. Soc. Am.* **51**:520.

Hubel, H. 1971. The visual cortex of the brain. In *Contemporary Psychology.* Readings from Scientific American. W. H. Freeman and Company, San Francisco.

Hutchins, C. M., and F. L. Fielding. 1968. Acoustical measurements of violins. *Phys. Today* **21**(No. 7):34.

John, E. R. 1972. Switchboard versus statistical theories of learning and memory. *Science* **177**:850.

Keller, J. B. 1953. Bowing of violin strings. *Comm. on Pure and Applied Math.* **6**:483.

Klein, W., R. Plomp, and L. C. W. Pols. 1970. Vowel spectra, vowel spaces and vowel identification. *J. Acoust. Soc. Am.* **48**:999.

Plomp, R. 1964. The ear as a frequency analyzer. *J. Acoust. Soc. Am.* **36**:1628.

Plomp, R. 1970. Timbre as a multidimensional attribute of complex tones. In *Frequency Analysis and Periodicity Detection in Hearing.* R. Plomp and F. G. Smoorenburg, eds. A. W. Suithoff, Leiden.

Plomp, R., and H. J. M. Steeneken. 1971. Pitch versus timbre. Proc. Seventh Int. Congr. Acoust., Budapest.

Plomp, R., and H. J. M. Steeneken. 1972. Place dependence of timbre in reverberant sound fields. Institute for Perception RVO-TNO, Report No. 15.

Reinicke, W., and L. Cremer. 1970. Application of holographic interferometry to vibrations of the bodies of string instruments. *J. Acoust. Soc. Am.* **48**:988.

Schumacher, R. T. 1972. Carnegie Mellon University, *private communication.*

Simmons, F. B. 1970. Monaural processing. In *Foundations of Modern Auditory Theory.* J. V. Tobias, ed. Academic Press, New York.

CHAPTER 5

SUPERPOSITION AND SUCCESSIONS OF COMPLEX TONES AND THE PERCEPTION OF MUSIC

In the course of Chapters 2, 3 and 4 we have been moving gradually up the ladder of neural processing of acoustical signals, from the mechanisms leading to the perception of primary pitch, subjective pitch, loudness, and timbre, and to the recognition of a musical instrument. On the physical side, we have analyzed how the sound characteristics leading to these sensations are actually generated in musical instruments. These psychological attributes are necessary, but by no means sufficient, ingredients of music. Music is made of *successions* and *superpositions* of tones that convey certain meanings (Gestalt) which can be analyzed, stored, and compared in the brain. An objective study of the neuropsychology of these higher order processes is practically nonexistent. The reader no doubt already has sensed how much guesswork was involved in the discussion of the perception of timbre (Section 4.8). We are in much worse shape when it comes to the higher psychological attributes such as consonance, dissonance, the sense of tonality and return, and, in the end, the whole gamut of emotional reactions to music.

We mentioned in Chapter 1 that, very likely, music did emerge as a byproduct or spinoff of the evolution of speech and language and the associated neural network capabilities. This seems to suggest, therefore, that the neuropsychology of speech and language should be studied exhaustively first and that only then should the acquired knowledge be "translated" or "transformed" to homologous musical information-processing operations. We are not ready to do this, however, nor would we have sufficient space in this book. This is why we are forced to keep our discussion in far more conventional and restricted bounds in this chapter.

5.1 Superposition of Complex Tones

Polyphonic music consists of superpositions of complex tones. Even if only a single melody is played in monophonic music, a superposition of reverberant sounds usually reaches our ear, leading to the superposition of complex tones. The psychophysical study of complex tone superposition effects is still very much incomplete. This applies particularly to the understanding of how the ear and the brain are able to disentangle the "mess" of frequencies that belong to different simultaneously sounding complex tones, so as to keep the sensations of these tones apart. Here, we can only present a qualitative and oversimplified discussion.

When two complex tones of different pitch are superposed, either of two situations may arise: the fundamental frequency of the higher tone is equal to one of the upper harmonics of the lower tone, or it is not. In the first case, the upper tone will reinforce certain upper harmonics of the lower tone. Why don't we, then, simply detect a change in *quality* of the lower tone, instead of clearly singling out the upper tone and even keeping the quality of both tones apart? A similar problem arises with the second case where each tone produces its own multiplicity of resonance regions on the basilar membrane. How does our brain single out from the resulting mixture which sequence belongs to what tone? For instance, consider the superposition of two complex tones, say, A_2 (110 Hz) and $C_3\#$ (140) Hz. The harmonics of both tones are shown in Fig. 5.1 on a linear frequency scale. For each one of

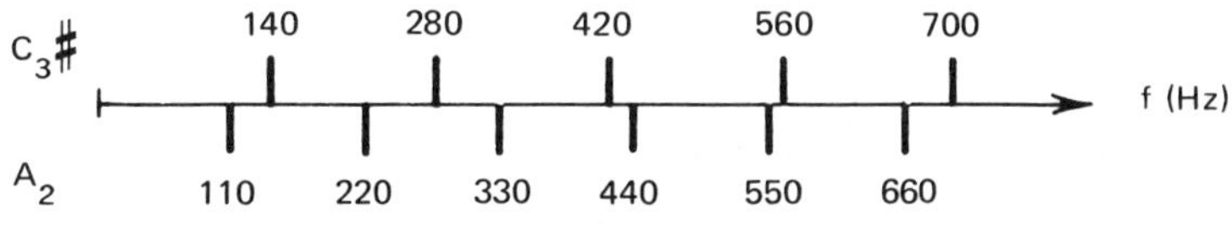

Fig. 5.1

these frequencies there is a corresponding resonance region on the basilar membrane (Fig. 2.8). The sensor cells do not get the slightest clue as to which tone each resonance region belongs to. This discrimination must therefore be performed at a higher center in the auditory neural pathway.

The *pitch* of the two tones is probably discriminated via the periodicity pitch mechanism (Sections 2.7 and 4.8). Any two arbitrary frequencies of the components shown in Fig. 5.1 define a repetition rate that in principle could lead to a pitch sensation (Section 2.7). By just looking at the spacings between components in Fig. 5.1, one can easily realize that a great variety of different repetition rates may thus be engendered, particularly in the low frequency range. However, there are pairs of components that always lead to, and hence reinforce, the same fundamental frequencies of 110 and 140 Hz and their multiples: these are precisely the pairs belonging to the *same* tone! In other words, the repetition rate detection mechanism, although bewildered by a variety of repetition rates, still seems to be able to single out and "lock in" on the most prominent features of the vibration pattern and generate the corresponding periodicity pitch signals, overruling the (highly confused) primary pitch detection system.

A most astounding capability of the auditory neural system is that of discriminating the *quality* of two simultaneously sounding complex tones. No real music would be possible without such capability. For instance, assume that you listen monaurally with earphones to the sound of instrument 1 playing *exactly* the note A_4, and instrument 2 playing *exactly* A_5, at nearly the same intensity level. Fig. 5.2 shows the hypo-

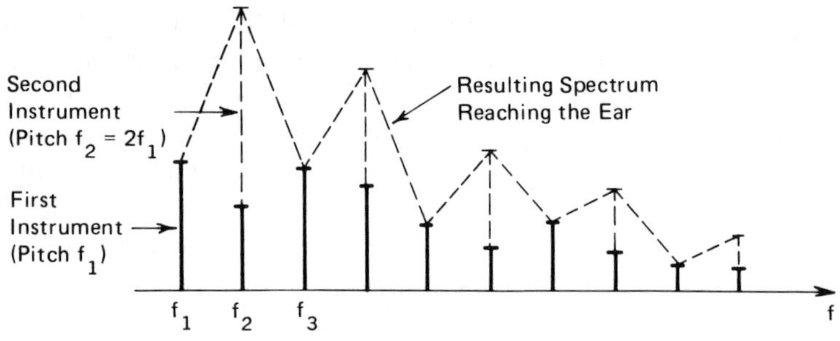

Fig. 5.2

thetical superposition. The total length of the vertical bars represents the total intensity of each harmonic actually reaching the ear. How does our brain manage to keep both tones apart, in terms of quality? This discrimination mechanism is not at all understood; a *time element* seems to play the key role. First, the initiation (attack) of two "simultaneous" tones is never exactly synchronized, nor does the tone buildup develop in the same manner, particularly if both tones come from different directions (stereo effect). During this transient period, the processing mechanism in our brain seems able to lock in on certain characteristic features of each instrument's vibration pattern and to keep track of these features, even if they are garbled and blurred by the signal from the other instrument. During performance, too, slight excursions in frequency and intensity (the so-called *chorus* effect) that are *coherent* for the whole harmonic series of each tone are used by the auditory processing mechanism to trigger the right neural readout signals for each instrument (Section 4.8). Other, more pronounced, variations that seem to provide important clues to the mechanism for discriminating tone quality are the periodic variations in pitch (vibrato) and intensity (tremolo, vibrato) that can be evoked (voluntarily or involuntarily) in otherwise steady tones of many musical instruments. Superposition of multiple complex sounds totally deprived of these small coherent time-dependent perturbations—as happens when multiple stops are combined in organ music—are indeed much more difficult to discriminate in quality.

138

What probably aids the discrimination mechanism of both pitch and quality of complex tones the most is the information received from a *progression* of tone superpositions. In such a case not only the above mentioned "primary" cues given by the coherent fluctuations in timing and frequency of each tone can be used, but the "higher order" or secondary information extracted from the melodic lines (the musical "messages") played by each instrument (see also p. 130) will also be available.

The complex tone discrimination mechanism has its equivalent (and probably, its origin) in the mechanism that steers our auditory perception when we follow the speech of one given person among many different conversations conducted simultaneously at similar sound levels.[1] This ability has been pointedly called the "cocktail party effect," and very likely uses the same cues, primary and secondary, as the complex tone discrimination mechanism. Finally, it probably is this same mechanism which enables us to disentangle individual sounds from among the messy tone superposition in a reverberating hall (Section 4.6). In this latter case, it is again a time effect that seems to play the main role: the "first" arrival of the direct sound (Figs. 4.26 and 27) provides the key cues on which our perception system locks in to define the actual tone sensation and tone discrimination. This is called the *precedence* effect in room acoustics.

Visual discriminatory and "lock-in" tasks are performed at a lower level in the "superior colliculus" of the midbrain (Gordon 1972), a nucleus of neurons of the sensory pathway, where incoming signals from the retina and outgoing signals from the cortex can interact with each other, giving feedback instructions from the latter a chance to influence or control the processing of the former. Very likely, a similar mechanism handles the cortex feedback-controlled lock-in operations in the auditory pathway.

As happens with two pure tones, there is a minimum difference in fundamental frequency that two complex tones must have in order to be heard out separately. When two complex tones differ in pitch less than the limit for tone discrimination, first order beats (Section 2.4) may arise between all harmonics. If, for instance, both complex tones are out-of-tune unisons with fundamental frequencies f_1 and $f_1 + \epsilon$, respectively, *all* resonance regions will overlap on the basilar membrane and produce beats of different frequencies. The fundamentals will beat with frequency ϵ, the second harmonics with frequency 2ϵ, and so on. Only the first few harmonics are important; usually the beats of the fundamental (ϵ) are the most pronounced. First order beats between corresponding harmonics will also appear if we superpose two complex tones forming other mistuned musical intervals. These are quite different

---

[1] Note, however, that language processing is accomplished mainly in the *left* cerebral hemisphere (Geschwind 1972), whereas musical operations probably involve mainly the right side.

(though equal in frequency) from the second order beats that arise in out-of-tune intervals of *pure* tones (Section 2.6).

5.2 The Sensation of Musical Consonance and Dissonance

Consonance and dissonance are subjective feelings associated with two (or more) simultaneously sounding tones, of a nature much less well defined than the psychophysical variables of pitch and loudness, and even quality. Whereas there is a relatively small variance among individual judgments regarding the latter, there is a much wider disparity when a given group of subjects judges the "consonance" or "dissonance" of musical intervals. Furthermore, learning and experience play a very important role in judgments of consonance.

When two complex tones are sounded in unison or in an octave exactly in tune, *all* harmonics of the second tone will pair up exactly with harmonics of the first tone; no "intermediate" frequencies will be introduced by the second tone. This property puts the octave in a very special situation as a musical interval (in addition to the arguments concerning vibration pattern simplicity put forth in the analysis of pure tone superpositions in Section 2.7). The situation changes when we sound a perfect fifth of complex tones (Table 5.1):

Table 5.1

Tonic	*Perfect fifth*
f	
	$f_1' = \tfrac{3}{2}f_1$
$2f_1$	
$3f_1$ --------	$f_2' = 3f_1$
$4f_1$	
	$f_3' = \tfrac{9}{2}f_1$
$5f_1$	
$6f_1$ --------	$f_4' = 6f_1$

All odd harmonics of the fifth have frequencies that lie *between* harmonics of the tonic; only its even harmonics coincide. In particular, the third harmonic of the fifth, of frequency $\tfrac{9}{2}f_1$, lies "dangerously close" to the frequencies of the fourth and the fifth harmonic of the tonic: their resonance regions on the basilar membrane may overlap and either beats or "roughness" may thus appear (Section 2.4), even if the interval of fundamental frequencies is perfectly in tune. By constructing tables similar to Table 5.1, the reader may verify for himself that for such other musical intervals as the fourth, thirds, and sixths the proportion of "colliding" harmonics increases rapidly and moves down in harmonic order. Historically, this effect was thought to be the cause for the sensations of consonance and dissonance.

Indeed, since the times of von Helmholtz, dissonance was associated with the number, intensity, and frequency of beating harmonics—and consonance with the absence thereof. In other words, it was assumed that for some unspecified reason our auditory system "does not like beats." As a result, it prefers, above all, the perfect unison and the perfect octave because in these intervals all harmonics of the upper tone form matching pairs with harmonics of the tonic. In the fifth, according to Table 5.1, the third harmonic of the upper tone may beat with the fourth and fifth harmonics of the tonic. The increasing proportion of beating pairs of harmonics that appear as one proceeds to the fourth, the sixths and thirds, the sevenths, the seconds, etc., would thus explain the decreasing consonance—or increasing dissonance—of these intervals. This assumption was particularly attractive because—as it is easy to show mathematically—in order to maximize the number of matching harmonics of two complex tones (and hence minimize that of nonmatching ones), it is necessary that their fundamental frequencies f_1 and f_1' *be in the ratio of integer numbers,* and that these numbers *be as small as possible.* Indeed, if

$$\frac{f_1'}{f_1} = \frac{n}{m} \qquad n, \; m: \text{integers} \tag{5.1}$$

then the mth harmonic of f_1' will have the same frequency as the nth harmonic of f_1: $mf_1' = nf_1$ [and so will the $(2 \times m)^{th}$ with the $(2 \times n)^{th}$, etc.]. All other harmonics will not match and thus may give beats if their frequencies are near enough to each other. Table 5.2 shows the intervals within one octave that can be formed with small numbers m, n and which are accepted in the Western musical culture as consonances (in decreasing order of "perfection"):

Table 5.2

Frequency ratio n/m		Interval
"Perfect" Consonances	1/1	unison
	2/1	octave
	3/2	fifth
	4/3	fourth
"Imperfect" Consonances	5/3	major sixth
	5/4	major third
	6/5	minor third
	8/5	minor sixth

141

On the basis of more recent and more sophisticated monaural and binaural experiments (Plomp and Levelt 1965) on consonance judgment involving pairs of pure tones and inharmonic complex tones, it became apparent that beats between harmonics may not be the major determining factor in the perception of consonance. Two pure tones an octave or less apart were presented to a number of musically naive (untrained) subjects who were supposed to give a qualification as to the "consonance" or "pleasantness" of the superposition. A *continuous* pattern was obtained, that did not reveal preference for any particular musical interval. An example is shown in Fig. 5.3. Whenever the pure tones were less

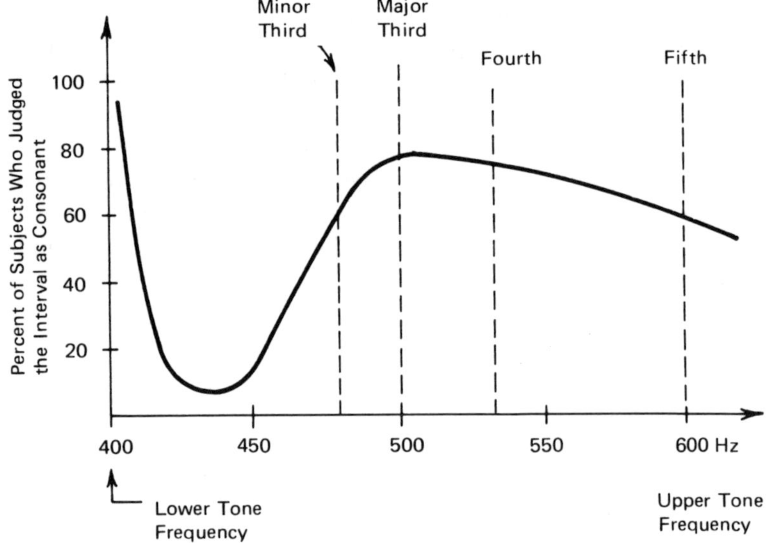

Fig. 5.3

than about a minor third apart, they were judged "dissonant" (except for the unison); intervals equal or larger than a minor third were judged as more or less consonant, irrespective of the actual frequency ratio.[2] The shape of the curve really depends on the absolute frequency of the fixed tone. All this is related to the "roughness" sensation of out-of-tune unisons and to the critical band discussed in Section 2.4. The results of these experiments may be summarized as follows: (1) When the frequencies of two pure tones fall *outside* the critical band, the corresponding pure tone interval is judged to be "consonant." (2) When they coincide, they are judged as "perfectly" consonant. (3) When their frequencies differ by an amount ranging from about 5% to 50% of the corresponding critical bandwidth, they are judged as "nonconsonant."

---

[2] Trained musicians were excluded from this experiment, because they would have been strongly compelled to identify consonances on the basis of training.

We shall call an interval of two pure tones under these latter conditions a "basic dissonance."

We now turn back to the musically more significant case of two simultaneously sounding *complex* tones and apply the above results individually to each pair of neighboring upper harmonics.[3] If the total number of pairs that are more or less consonant [see (1) above] and perfectly consonant (2) is weighted against that of basic dissonances (3), a "consonance index" may be obtained for each interval of complex tones (Plomp and Levelt 1965). It can be shown that this index indeed happens to attain peak values for tones whose fundamental frequencies satisfy condition (5.1): the height of the peaks ("degree" of consonance) follows approximately the decreasing order given in Table 5.2. Moreover, in view of the dependence of the critical bandwidth on frequency (Fig. 2.13) *a given musical interval has a degree of consonance that varies along the frequency range.* In particular, moving toward lower frequencies a given musical interval becomes less and less consonant—a fact well known in polyphonic music, where in the bass register mainly octaves and, eventually, fifths are used.

The degree of consonance depends on the quality or spectrum of the component tones, i.e., the *relative intensity* of dissonant vs. consonant upper harmonics. This, too, is well known in music: there are instrument combinations that "blend" together better than others in polyphonic music. Even the *order* in which two instruments define a musical interval is relevant. For instance, if a clarinet and a violin sound a major third, with the clarinet playing the lower note, the first dissonant pair of harmonics will be the 7th harmonic of the clarinet with the 6th harmonic of the violin (because only odd harmonics of the clarinet are present, Sections 4.4,5). This interval sounds smooth. If, on the other hand, the clarinet is playing the upper tone, the 3rd harmonic of the latter will collide with the 4th harmonic of the violin tone, and the interval will sound "harsh."

A more recent study of the perception of musical intervals (Houtsma and Goldstein 1971, 1972) invokes the almighty periodicity pitch mechanism as operating in consonance perception, too. This mechanism, which quite universally seeks to determine the rates at which vibration pattern features are repeated (Section 2.8), has an increasingly more difficult task to perform, the farther down in the harmonic ranking (Table 5.2) a given superposition of two complex tones belongs. This is quite simple to show mathematically.

There are more complicated factors influencing the sensation of consonance, most notably experience and training and the ensuing prejudice (i.e., musical tradition). It is interesting to note that, historically, musical

---

[3] This procedure is meaningful only if applied to harmonics *up to the seventh order;* above that, pairs of harmonics are basic dissonances even within the *same* tone.

intervals as explicit harmonic ingredients have been gradually "accepted" in Western civilization in an order close to the one given in Table 5.2: unison, octaves and fifths in Gregorian chant; the appearance of thirds and sixths around the 11th century, the increased usage of major sevenths in the Baroque and the acceptance of outright dissonances in present times. This seems to point to a gradual refinement and tolerance of our auditory processing ability, which now is amenable to "digest" a much more complicated input (as the vibration patterns of dissonances are) than a thousand years ago, when a fifth was probably considered a daring innovation. Of course, this was not the result of biological evolution but, rather, that of a sophistication of the *learning* experiences to which humans were being exposed as time went on. This development, as that of civilization as a whole, went on stepwise, in "quantum" jumps: it always took the mind of a genius-revolutionary to introduce daring innovations whose comprehension required new and more complex information-processing operations of the brain, and it was the greatness of the genius that was needed to persuade humanity to learn, and thus to accept, these daring innovations. While in Western music this evolution led to a transition from abstract forms (corresponding to simple auditory input patterns) to concrete (complex-patterned) forms, in the other arts, like painting, the development went from concrete forms (easily interpretable) to abstract ones. One may be tempted to speculate that this particular development of music should perhaps indicate a gradual shift of musical processing from the minor (right-side) cerebral hemisphere to the language-processing left hemisphere, which is better trained (and may be even better equipped) from the outset for complex auditory pattern analysis.

Finally, we must point out that there is also a strong *dynamical* component to the perception of consonance and dissonance, related to the "urge to resolve" certain dissonant tone combinations. "Tired" of the more difficult identification operations that are required for dissonances, the auditory neural processing system, in particular the periodicity pitch mechanism, may be "longing" for a simpler pattern to analyze.

So far we have been considering musical intervals smaller than, or equal to, the octave. For larger intervals (e.g., C_3–G_5) it is customary to project the upper tone down by octaves (G_5–G_4–G_3) until an interval smaller than one octave is obtained (C_3–G_3). The degree of consonance of that latter interval is then considered "equivalent" to that of the original one. This cyclical property of intervals that repeats within successive octaves has been called the *chroma* of musical tones. It is a basic property that assigns an equivalent ranking to all tones whose pitch differs by one or more octaves. What is responsible for this curious cyclic character of musical tones, which repeats every octave (every time the frequency doubles)? It obviously is related to the key property of the almighty octave: that of having all its harmonics coincident with upper harmonics of the fundamental. There is no other musical interval with this property (except the unison, of course); any other interval will introduce "colliding" harmonics. When perceiving tones that are one or several octaves apart, our neural processing mechanism (e.g., repetition rate detection) only requires a minimum of operations, whereas any other musical interval will demand an additional number of operations (to get rid of "parasitical" repetition rates). This may be why we value tones that are one, two or more octaves apart as of similar "ranking," calling their pitch by the same name.

Finally, when *three or more* tones are sounded together it is customary to analyze the resulting chord into pairs of tones and consider their individual consonance "values." It is obvious that, as more and more complex tones are added together, a more complicated configuration of resonance regions arises on the basilar membrane. Overlap will increase to the extent that sensor cells covering a large extension of the basilar membrane will respond all at the same time. Probably, it is mainly information on the repetition rates and their progression in time that keeps the vast amount of neural signals to the brain "intelligible." There is a limit to this intelligibility, though. When the vibration patterns are randomized (i.e., their periodicity is destroyed), or when their complexity exceeds a certain threshold, the neural processing mechanism simply gives up: no definite pitch and quality sensations can be established. The ensuing sensation is called *noise*. Any nonperiodic pressure oscillation leads to a noise sensation. Noise can, however, be highly organized. Just as a periodic oscillation can be analyzed into a discrete superposition of pure harmonic oscillations of frequencies that are integer multiples of the fundamental frequency (Section 4.3), aperiodic vibrations can be analyzed as a *continuous* superposition of pure vibrations of *all* possible frequencies. Depending on how the intensity is distributed among all possible frequencies, we obtain different *spectra of noise*. Noise plays a key role in the formation of consonants in speech. But it also plays a role in music; the importance of noise components in percussion instruments is obvious. The noise burst detected during the first tenths of a second in a piano and harpsichord tone has been shown to be a key element in the recognition process. The effect of noises of electronically controlled spectra on our auditory perception is being studied extensively with tone and noise synthesizers. A vast new territory in auditory sensations (music??) is now being unveiled.

5.3 Why Are There Musical Scales and Why Do We Enjoy Music?

Our ear is sensitive to sound waves over a wide range of frequencies. We can detect very minor changes in frequency; the just noticeable difference is typically of only 0.5% or less (Fig. 2.9). Yet our Western music (and that of most other cultures) is based on *scales,* i.e., tone transitions and tone superpositions differing from each other by more than 20 times the limen of our frequency resolution capability. Why don't we make music with continuously changing pitches that sound like, for instance, the "songs" of whales and dolphins (which have a very sophisticated acoustical communications system based on continuous frequency "sweeps")? Why does pitch always have to "jump" in discrete steps?

There is no simple answer to this question. First, let us remember that a given musical tone has to last a certain minimum amount of time in order to be processable by the brain (Section 3.4). This has prevented sweeping tones from becoming basic and lasting elements of music. Second, let us note that different musical cultures are using or have used different scales—thus scales are somehow related to, or were influenced by training and tradition. Historically, the existence of scales has been justified on the basis of consonance. This would imply that scales appeared in connection with polyphonic music. However, scales had already been in use when melodies were only sung (and/or accompanied) monophonically in unison (or, at the most, in octaves or fifths). A possibility has been suggested, that reverberation in halls or caves kept sounds for long enough (Section 4.7) so that even for monophonic music tone superpositions occurred and, hence, influenced the selection of pitches on the basis of consonance.

More likely, what matters is a "reverberation" in the *neural system,* an effect related to short term memory storage and identification processes, in which information on the incoming acoustical vibration is somehow kept in a "holding pattern" for a very short time, thus giving chance to superpositions of the incoming messages (closed-looped engrams, p. 133). Since at least part of the information is coded in the form of distribution of time intervals between successive neural impulses (integer multiples of the period, for a pure sinusoidal sound wave, Section 2.8), a superposition of tones whose frequency (or period) ratio is that of small integer numbers (relation 5.1) would give rise to a superposition of neural firings that is simpler, hence "easier to handle." In summary, we believe that there are scales because it is easier for the brain to process, identify, and store in its memory a melody that is made up of a time sequence of discrete pitch values that bear a certain relationship to each other, rather than one that sweeps continuously up and down over all possible frequencies, whose processing, identification, and storage in the memory would require far more information "bits" than a discrete sequence.

The "explanation" of scales on the basis of consonance, be it acoustical or neural, is not entirely satisfactory. The tones of melodies do not jump in octaves, fifths or fourths; most often, they proceed in half tones

146

and whole tones, both of which are dissonances. Thus what is likely to be superposed (in a hall or cave, or in the brain) are these dissonances. For this reason, the explanation of the existence of scales, i.e., discrete tone sequences, has also been attempted on a *dynamic* basis of tone-tone relationships in time. This line of thought is based on the musically so important, but psychophysically almost totally unexplored field of the sensations of "direction" of a two- (or more) tone sequence, of "dominance" of a given pitch therein and of "return" to that leading pitch (also called "finality"). For instance, we tend to assign a "natural" direction to a two-tone sequence that is upward (in pitch) if the tones are a semitone apart, and downward, if they are a whole tone apart. In both cases, we assign a dominance to the second tone; the "natural" sense is then equivalent to the direction toward, the contranatural to the direction away from, the dominant. Similarly, a sequence like C-G-C-G-C-G- . . . . . "wants" to be ended on C, whereas the sequence C-F-C-F-C-F- . . . . . "cries" for an F as the terminating note. And if we listen to E-G-E-G- . . . . neither of the components is satisfactory as an ending—we want to hear C! The whole diatonic orientation of Western music listening is based on these effects, and so is the "meaning" (the tonal "Gestalt") of musical messages (Section 1.3).

At the beginning of this century, Lipps (1905) and Meyer (1900) attempted to "explain" the preference for certain melodic endings and tonic dominance in terms of numerical properties of the frequency ratios of a two-tone "melody." In the above examples, the dominating tone is that one whose frequency corresponds to a power of two in the integer number ratio. For instance, $f_G/f_C = \frac{3}{2}$; $f_F/f_C = \frac{4}{3}$; $f_C/f_B = \frac{16}{15}$. Later investigations, however, have tended to attribute these effects mainly to cultural conditioning (Lundin 1967). Still, the question remains: Why did these and not any other preferences emerge?

We may venture the prediction that all these effects probably arise in the neural system's "minimum-effort way" of operating: in the identification process of musical (and other sensorial) messages, the system first discards all but a certain minimum of information cues. If the identification has been successful it proceeds ahead with the next message. If not, it goes back and searches for additional cues. This applies not only to a single one-tone input, but also to the musical message as a whole: *the nervous system tries to use whatever information is available from previous experiences (e.g., memory-stored messages) to facilitate and even anticipate the identification process of new incoming information.* This "prediction" or "extrapolation" capability—quite generally, perhaps the most essential operation of the central nervous system helping to enhance the chance of survival for all higher living beings—has been confirmed through electrophysiological measurements (John 1972 and references therein): When a certain event in a previously learned succession of stimuli is expected but does not occur, cortical activity (Section 4.8) appears at a latency similar to that usually evoked by the expected event. This capability was also confirmed in speech-processing studies (Chistovich 1962). Thus, whenever this prediction mechanism fails during the perception of music (e.g., because of an "unexpected" passage or a goof in the performance), the extra work required for reidentification gives a particular sensation of "musical tension" (Roederer 1972).

Quite generally, it is possible that the combined effect of complexity of tone message identification (i.e., the total number of required neural operations per unit time) and the associations triggered in other brain centers might be the ultimate "cause" of the musical sensations evoked by a given musical message. For instance, when the tonality of a musical piece is modulated, the auditory nervous system must quickly build up a new "checklist" for the tonal identification operations expected to come. This rapid buildup, an extra load of probably hundreds of thousands of individual operations, would yield the particular musical sensation related to tonality change. Since this rearrangement probably occurs anyway, involuntarily, even if we know the musical piece by heart, the musical sensation appears every time—quite fortunately for music lovers. *Unmusical* individuals, who are unable to experience these sensations, probably are subjects whose musical message identification mechanism has not had a chance to develop its potentialities to full capability. Hence, although they *hear* everything that highly musical subjects hear, their central auditory system can only handle a reduced amount of acoustical information in a given time. A tonality change passes unnoticed because even for a fixed tonality their auditory processing mechanism is probably saturated with an information flow that exceeds its processing capacity.

In the above discussion we have left out all aspects related to emotionality as an overall "output" of musical perception. This effect is the result of a process of integral comparison of the incoming messages with previous musical experiences and the retrieval of information on, i.e., the "replay" of, the circumstances under which they had been experienced. We shall not proceed any further with this purely psychological topic, except to point out that memory storage of acoustical experiences and associations may start at a very early age—as a matter of fact, in the late intrauterine stage (Benenzon 1971), with the fetus perceiving the mother's heartbeat, voice, and gastric sounds, as well as external sounds, filtered through the amniotic fluid.

Also left out was any reference to rhythm as a most fundamental component of music. This is a particularly critical omission, because the appearance of rhythm always seems to have been the first step in the evolution of a given musical culture. The propagation through cerebral tissue of a cyclically changing flux of neural signals triggered by rhythmic sound patterns may somehow enter in "resonance" with the natural "clocks" of the brain that control body functions and behavioral response. These clocks probably work on the basis of neural activity traveling in closed-looped circuits or engrams, or in any other neural wiring schemes that have natural periods of cyclic response. Much more research is needed before we can venture to give a clear-cut reply to the question formulated in the title of this section: why do we enjoy music?

5.4 Building Musical Scales

We conclude this last chapter with a more or less conventional discussion of musical scales. Let us accept the fact that scales do exist, and for a purely practical purpose, let us simply define a scale as *a discrete set of pitches arranged in such a way as to yield a maximum possible number of consonant combinations* (or minimum possible number of dissonances) *when two or more notes of the set are sounded together.* With this definition, and keeping in mind Table 5.2, it is possible to generate at once two scales in an almost unequivocal way, depending on whether all consonant intervals are to be taken into account, or whether only the "perfect" consonances are to be considered. In the first case, we get the *just scale;* in the second we get the *Pythagorean scale.*

1. *The just scale*

We start with a tone of frequency f_1, which we call *do.*[4] The first most obvious thing to do is to introduce the octave above, which we denote as *do'.* This yields the most consonant interval of all. The next obvious thing is to add the fifth of frequency $\frac{3}{2}f_1$, which we call *sol.* That yields two new consonant intervals, besides the octave, of frequency ratios $\frac{3}{2}$ (do–sol) and $\frac{4}{3}$ (the fourth sol–do'), respectively. For the next step there are two choices, if we want to keep a maximum number of consonant intervals. They are the notes $\frac{5}{4}f_1$ or $\frac{6}{5}f_1$, which we call mi and mi ♭, respectively. We choose the first one, *mi,* because this will guarantee a number of consonances of higher "degree". Fig. 5.4 shows the resulting intervals, all of them consonant. The notes do–mi–sol constitute the *major triad,* the building stone of Western music harmony (our second choice $\frac{6}{5}f_1$ or mi ♭ would have yielded a *minor triad.*)

This is so important, that a short discussion on the major triad is in order. Notice that the fundamental frequencies of its notes are the 4th, 5th, and 6th components of the harmonic series of $f_0 = f_1/4$ (two octaves

---

[4] The solfeggio notation do–re–mi–fa–sol–la–ti–do is used here to indicate *relative* position in a scale (i.e., the chroma), not actual pitch.

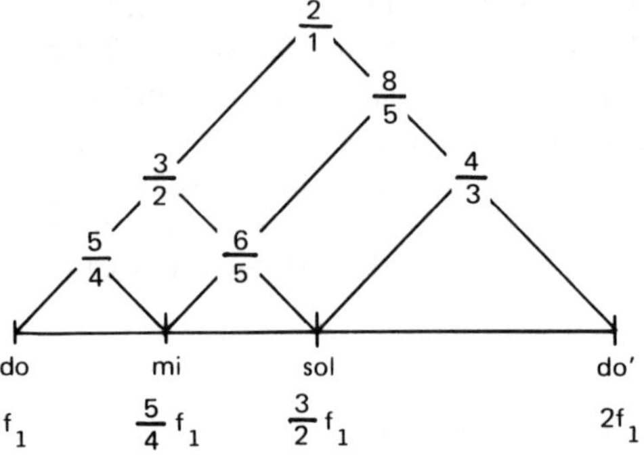

Fig. 5.4

below *do*). This latter frequency thus represents the common repetition rate of the pairs do–mi, mi–sol, and is thus heard as a subjective (missing) fundamental (Section 2.7). The repetition rate of the pair do–sol is $f_1/2$, i.e., one octave below do. The major triad thus strongly reinforces via the fundamental tracking mechanism the "chroma" of its tonic. This does not happen with the minor triad, do–mi♭–sol, whose components, taken in pairs, define *three* different repetition rates, each one corresponding to a different chroma. More research is needed to find out whether this fact is in some way related to the markedly different "character" of major and minor triads (and tonalities).

We may continue to "fill in" tones, in each step trying to keep the number of dissonances to a minimum and the number of consonances (Table 5.2) to a maximum. We end up with the *just diatonic scale* of seven notes within the octave (Fig. 5.5). These seven notes can be

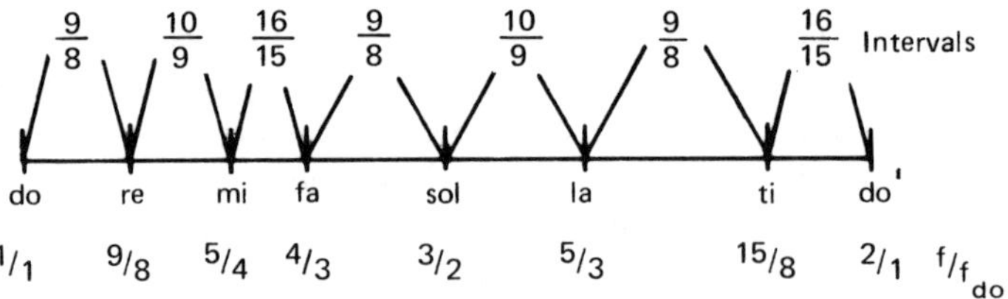

Fig. 5.5. The just diatonic scale.

projected in octaves up and down to form a full diatonic scale over the whole compass of audible pitch. Notice in Fig. 5.5 the two intervals of quite similar frequency ratios ⁹⁄₈ and ¹⁰⁄₉, representing *whole tones*. The interval ¹⁶⁄₁₅ defines a *semitone*. With the notes of this scale, taken in pairs, we can form 16 consonant intervals (Table 5.4), 10 dissonant intervals (minor and major sevenths, diminished fifth, whole tones, semitones) and—rather unfortunately—*two "out-of-tune"* consonances:

the 1.5% too sharp minor third re–fa ($^{32}/_{27}$) and the 1.9% too flat fifth re–la ($^{40}/_{27}$). Finally, and perhaps most important, with the just diatonic scale we can form four just major triads: do–mi–sol, mi–sol–ti, fa–la–do′ and sol–ti–re′, two just minor triads: mi–sol–ti and la–do′–mi′, and an "out-of-tune" minor triad re–fa–la.

Considering the existence of uneven spacings between neighboring notes, it is possible to still implement this scale by parting the larger gaps (whole tones) into two semitones each. Unfortunately, the resulting new intervals get more and more complex (e.g., several kinds of semitones, more out-of-tune consonances), the choices are not unique, and different frequency values result for the so-called *enharmonic* equivalents do# – re♭, re# –mi♭, etc. Seeking to keep the proportion of possible consonances to a maximum, the following notes are introduced: mi♭ ($^{6}/_{5}f_1$), ti♭ ($^{9}/_{5}f_1$), sol# ($^{25}/_{16}f_1$) (or la♭, $^{8}/_{5}f_1$), do# ($^{25}/_{24}f_1$) and fa# ($^{45}/_{32}f_1$). The result is a *chromatic just scale* of 12 notes within the octave.

2. *The Pythagorean scale*

We now restrict ourselves to the so-called perfect consonances, the just fifth and the just fourth (and the octave, of course), and build our scale on the basis of these intervals alone. We may proceed in the following way. After introducing *sol* we move a just fifth down from do′ to introduce *fa* ($^{2}/_{3} \times 2f_1 = ^{4}/_{3}f_1$). Then we move a just fourth down from sol to obtain *re* ($^{3}/_{4} \times ^{3}/_{2}f_1 = ^{9}/_{8}f_1$), and a fifth up from the latter to get *la* ($^{3}/_{2} \times ^{9}/_{8}f_1 = ^{27}/_{16}f_1$). Finally we fill the remaining gaps by moving a fourth down from la to obtain *mi* ($^{3}/_{4} \times ^{27}/_{16}f_1 = ^{81}/_{64}f_1$) and up a fifth from there, to *ti* ($^{3}/_{2} \times ^{81}/_{64}f_1 = ^{243}/_{128}f_1$). The result is the so-called Pythagorean scale (Fig. 5.6). Notice that there is only *one* whole tone interval, the *Pythagorean whole tone* of frequency ratio $^{9}/_{8}$ (equal to the "short" whole tone of the just scale). The interval $^{256}/_{243}$ is the *Pythagorean diatonic semitone*.

We can convert this scale into a chromatic one, by continuing to jump up or down in just fourths and fifths. We thus obtain *fa#* (a

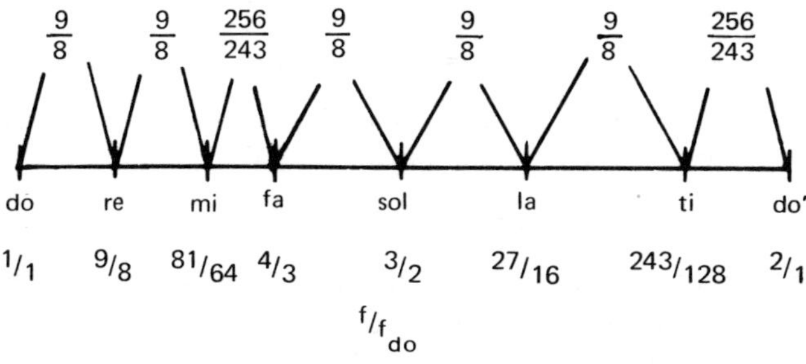

Fig. 5.6. The Pythagorean diatonic scale.

fourth below ti), *do*♯ (a fourth below fa♯), *sol*♯ (a fifth above do♯),
ti♭ (a fourth above fa) and *mi*♭ (a fifth below ti♭). In this way a new
semitone appears (e.g., fa-fa♯) defined by the odd-looking ratio
2,187/2,048, called the *Pythagorean chromatic semitone*. This whole pro-
cedure again leads to enharmonic equivalents of different frequency.
In particular, if we continue to move up and down in steps of just
fourths and fifths we eventually will come back to our initial note
do—but not exactly! In other words, we shall arrive at the enharmonic
equivalent "ti♯" whose frequency is *not* equal to that of do′ ($=2f_1$).

So, based on some "logical" principles, we have generated two scales.
Each one has its own set of problems. By far the most serious one is
the fact, common to both, that only a very limited group of tonalities
can be played with these scales without running into trouble with
out-of-tune consonances. In other words, *both scales impose very
serious transposition and modulation restrictions.* This was recognized
as early as in the 17th century. There is no doubt, though, that both
scales do reveal a quite specific character when music is performed on
instruments tuned to either of them. But the type of music that can
be played is extremely limited.

3. *The tempered scale*

It thus became apparent that a new scale was needed, which on
the basis of a reasonable compromise, giving up some of the "justness"
of musical intervals, would lead to *equally spaced intervals,* regardless
of the particular tonality. In other words, a semitone would have the
same frequency ratio, whether it was a do–do♯, a mi–fa or a la–ti♭,
and a fifth would be the same whether it was fa–do′ or do♯–sol♯.
This was accomplished in the *tempered scale,* enthusiastically sponsored
by none other than J. S. Bach, who composed a collection of Preludes
and Fugues ("Das wohltemperierte Clavier") with the specific purpose
of taking full advantage of the new frontiers opened up by unrestricted
possibilities of tonality change.

In the tempered scale the frequency ratio is the same for all 12
semitones lying between do and do′. Let us call *s* this ratio. This means
that

$$f_{\text{do}♯} = sf_{\text{do}}, \ f_{\text{re}} = sf_{\text{do}♯} = s^2 f_{\text{do}}, \ \ldots \ldots \ldots, \ f_{\text{do}′} = s^{12} f_{\text{do}}$$

Since we know that $f_{\text{do}′} = 2f_{\text{do}}$ (only the octave is kept as a "just"
interval!), the twelfth power of *s* must be equal to 2. Or

$$s = \sqrt[12]{2} = 1.0595 \tag{5.2}$$

This is the frequency ratio for a *tempered semitone.* The frequencies
that ensue for the notes of the chromatic tempered scale are *integer
powers of s* times f_{do}. Table 5.3 shows the frequency ratios for consonant
intervals in all three scales.

Table 5.3

Interval	Just Scale		Pythagorean Scale		Tempered Scale	
	ratio	cents	ratio	cents	ratio	cents
Octave	2.000	1200	2.000	1200	2.000	1200
Fifth	1.500	702	1.500	702	1.498	700
Fourth	1.333	498	1.333	498	1.335	500
Major third	1.250	386	1.265	408	1.260	400
Minor third	1.200	316	1.184	294	1.189	300
Major sixth	1.667	884	1.687	906	1.682	900
Minor sixth	1.600	814	1.580	792	1.587	800

It is convenient to introduce a standard subdivision of the basic interval of the tempered scale, in order to be able to express numerically the small differences between intervals pertaining to different scales. This subdivision, although of no application per se in music, is generally used to describe small changes in frequency (vibrato), changes in intonation (pitch), and out-of-tuneness of notes or intervals. Many subdivisions of the frequency scale have been proposed and used in the past. The most accepted procedure today is to divide the tempered semitone in *one hundred equal intervals,* or, what is equivalent, to divide the octave in twelve hundred equal parts. Since what defines a musical interval is the *ratio* of the fundamental frequencies of the component tones (not their difference), what must be done here is to divide the semitone frequency ratio s (5.2) into one hundred equal *factors* c:

$$\underbrace{c \times c \times c \times \cdots \times c}_{100 \text{ times}} = c^{100} = s$$

In view of relation (5.2) the value of c is

$$c = \sqrt[100]{1.0595} = 1.000578 \tag{5.3}$$

The unit of this subdivision is called a *cent*. To find out how many cents are "contained" in a given interval of arbitrary frequency ratio r, we must determine how many times we must multiply c with itself to obtain r:

$$c^n = r \tag{5.4}$$

n is then the "value" of r expressed in cents. By definition, one tempered semitone is 100 cents, a tempered whole tone (r^2) is 200 cents, a tempered fifth (r^7) is 700 cents, etc. To find the value in cents of any other interval we must use logarithms. Taking into account the properties described in Section 3.4, we take logarithms of relation (5.4):
$n \log c = \log r$.

153

Hence

$$n = \frac{\log r}{\log c} = 3{,}846 \log r \qquad (5.5)$$

Using this relation, we find the values in cents for the various consonant intervals that have been given in Table 5.3.

5.5 The Standard Scale and the Standard of Pitch

The tempered scale has been in use for more than 200 years and has de facto become the standard scale to which all instruments with fixed-pitch notes are tuned. Since its inception, though, it has come under attack on several occasions—until this day. The main target of these attacks is the "unjustness" of the consonant intervals of the tempered scale, particularly the thirds and sixths (Table 5.3), which do, indeed, sound a little bit out-of-tune when listened to carefully and persistently, especially in the bass register.

Let us critically compare the scales discussed in the previous section with each other. There is no doubt that for *one given tonality* the just scale is the "theoretically" perfect scale, yielding a maximum possibility of combinations of just or "pure" (i.e., beatless) intervals. For this reason, the just scale should indeed be taken as a sort of reference scale; this is precisely why we have introduced it in the first place. But the big question is: Does our auditory system really care for just, beatless intervals? And then: Would we give up tonality transposition and modulation possibilities in favor of obtaining these "pure" intervals? A 200-year history of music has answered these questions unmistakably with a loud and clear *no!* So the just scale is ruled out.

The Pythagorean scale may be one step forward in the right direction (while fifths and fourths are kept as just intervals, thirds and sixths are slightly out-of-tune, Table 5.3), but it still does not allow unlimited transposition and modulation possibilities. There have been other scales, introduced as minor modifications of the Pythagorean scale, that we will not even mention here, however. None has succeeded in preventing the tempered scale from being universally accepted.

There have been attempts to settle *experimentally* the question of which scale is really preferred (setting tonality modulation capability arguments aside). There are two possible approaches: (1) To use fixed-frequency instruments (piano, organ) and to carefully compare the subjective impressions of a given piece of music played successively on two instruments of the same kind, respectively tuned to different scales. The piece of music, of course, should be very simple, without modulations into distant tonalities. And the instrument really should be one with nondecaying tones (such as the organ) in order to bring out beats or roughness more clearly. (2) To measure experimentally the average frequencies of pitch-intonation chosen by singers or by performers of variable-pitch instruments (strings), and to determine whether they prefer one scale to another.

The second approach is more appropriate for yielding quantitative results. Recent electronic instrumentation has made possible very precise instantaneous frequency measurements on performers. The musical intervals to be watched closely are the major third and the major sixth, for which the differences between scales are most pronounced (Table 5.5). Notice, in particular, that the upper note in both of these intervals is flat in the just scale and sharp in the Pythagorean scale (with respect to the tempered scale). The experimental results very convincingly show that, on the average, singers and string players perform the upper notes of these intervals with *sharp* intonation (Ward 1970). This seems to point to a preference for the Pythagorean scale. However, one should not jump to conclusions: The same experiments revealed that also fifths and fourths and even the almighty octave were played or sung sharp, on the average![5] Rather than revealing a preference for a given scale (the Pythagorean), these experiments point to the existence of a previously unexpected *universal tendency to play or sing sharp all musical intervals*. Furthermore, a perhaps even more significant result of these experiments is that individual fluctuations of the pitch of a given note during the course of a performance are very large. This includes vibrato as well as variations of the average pitch of a given note when it reappears throughout the same piece of music. In these pitch fluctuations of a given written note, a frequency range is scanned that goes far beyond the frequency differences between different scales—actually, it makes the latter completely irrelevant! Should a listener have a subjective (probably unconscious) preference for a given scale or a given degree of "pureness" of musical intervals, those large pitch fluctuations would always feed him the "right" frequency for each note on which his auditory processing mechanism could lock in for the rest of the performance.

These results suggest that it may be more productive to turn to the first approach mentioned above and to try to analyze the subjective effect of the different scales on music played on *fixed-frequency* instruments tuned to these scales. Unfortunately, this can only be done qualitatively, and precise psychoacoustical measurements would be almost impossible to set up. Von Helmholtz did some experimentation with a reed organ and contended that the just entonation sounded clearly superior to any other. No systematic experiments have been done in recent times, although the availability of easily tunable electronic organs

---

[5] A reciprocal effect exists: Pure octaves are consistently judged by musicians to sound flat!

should make this task much easier. In the opinion of many musicians, there is a clear difference in the over-all subjective "character" of a musical piece played on an electronic organ in different tuning. This is due, in part, to the different character of beats (or absence thereof) of intervals played in the different scales. This difference appears noticeably enhanced when the loudness is increased substantially. This points to the appearance of combination tones and aural harmonics (Section 2.5) that get out of tune more markedly than the repetition rate when the original musical interval gets out of tune (Section 2.7).

So far, we have been dealing with intervals, i.e., frequency ratios. What about the absolute frequencies per se? Once a scale is adopted, it is sufficient to prescribe the frequency of only one note; it makes no difference which one. However, if musical instruments of fixed frequencies are to be easily interchangeable all over the world, this has to be done on the basis of an international agreement. One has prescribed for the "middle A" of the piano (A_4) a fundamental frequency of *440 Hz*. Different "regional" standard frequencies had been in use since the tuning fork became available in the 17th century. But, over the last two centuries, there has been a gradual rise of the "standard" frequency from about 415 Hz to as high as 461 Hz.[6] We can only hope that the present standard will, indeed, remain constant.

In the tempered scale, all intervals of the same kind (e.g., fifths, major thirds, etc.) are exactly "the same thing," except for the actual pitch of their components. A melody played in C major is in no way different from the same tune played in D major (except for the pitch range covered). Absolute "key colors" or different "moods" of certain tonalities have no psychoacoustical foundation, as experiments have shown (Corso 1957). There can be slight differences in the sounds of various keys, though, due to *physical* circumstances: the greater occurrence of black keys (which are struck in a slightly different way) in the piano for certain tonalities,[7] the greater occurrence of open strings for certain tonalities in string instruments, or the effect of the fixed frequency range of formants (Section 4.4) in soundboards and other resonance bodies.

One final word is in order on *absolute pitch perception*. The few persons endowed with the ability to recognize or to vocally reproduce a given note in absolute manner (this is also called "perfect" pitch) are usually greatly admired. It happens that *we have been trained to pay attention to, and to store in the long-term memory, only relative*

---

[6] This has a serious consequence for famous historical instruments that are still in use today. For instance, a Stradivarius violin, originally built for a standard pitch of, say, $A_4 = 415$ Hz, today has to be tuned higher, which means *higher tension* for the strings (relation 4.3). This alters the quality (spectrum) of the tone. A baroque organ, also built for $A_4 = 415$ Hz, when retuned to the higher pitch of $A_4 = 440$ Hz has to have its flue pipes partly cut, in order to shorten their effective length (relation 4.5).

[7] E.g., Chopin's piano music!

pitch intervals, because this is the information most relevant to a "musical message." In other words, our brain has been trained to interpret and store a melody as a sequence of pitch *transitions* rather than pitch "values"; the information on absolute pitch, although reaching our brain, is discarded as nonessential in the long-term assimilation process. It can, however, be retained by all normal persons during short intervals of time, ranging from 10 seconds up to a few minutes (Rakowski 1972). It is quite possible that "perfect pitch" could be learned at an early stage of mental education and retained thereafter, just as absolute color or smell recognition is "learned." These considerations and the surprising excursions in pitch detected electronically in live music, which seem to pass unnoticed by the listener, suggest the need for an operational re-definition of pitch as *the subjective correlate of each one of the acoustical events in a musically meaningful sequence of tones* (Houtsma and Goldstein 1971, 1972). It should come to no one's surprise that this is the definition that has been used—implicitly or explicitly—by musicians all the time!

References

Benenzon, R. O. 1971. *Musicoterapia y Educación,* Editorial Paidós, Buenos Aires.

Chistovich, L. A. 1962. Temporal course of speech sound perception. Proc. Fourth Int. Congr. Acoust., Copenhagen.

Corso, J. F. 1957. Absolute judgments of musical tonality. *J. Acoust. Soc. Am.* **29**:138.

Geschwind, N. 1972. Language and the brain. *Sci. Am.* **226**(no. 4):76.

Gordon, B. 1972. The superior colliculus of the brain. *Sci. Am.* **227**(no. 6):72.

Houtsma, A. J. M., and J. L. Goldstein. 1971. Perception of musical intervals: Evidence for the central origin of the pitch of complex tones. Massachusetts Institute of Technology, Research Laboratory of Electronics, Technical Report 484; 1972. *J. Acoust. Soc. Am.* **51**:520.

John, E. R. 1972. Switchboard versus statistical theories of learning and memory. *Science* **177**:850.

Lipps, T. 1905. *Psychologische Studien.* Durr'sche Buchhandlung, Leipzig. Discussed in R. W. Lundin, 1967.

Lundin, R. W. 1967. *An Objective Psychology of Music.* 2nd ed. The Ronald Press Company, New York.

Meyer, M. 1900. Elements of a psychological theory of melody. *Psychol. Rev.* **7**:241.

Plomp, R., and W. J. M. Levelt. 1965. Tonal consonance and critical bandwidth. *J. Acoust. Soc. Am.* **38**:548.

Rakowski, A. 1972. Direct comparison of absolute and relative pitch. Proc. Symp. on Hearing Theory, IPO Eindhoven.

Roederer, J. G. 1972. La musique, l'oreille et le cerveau. *Decouverte* 41 (May).

Ward, W. D. 1970. Musical perception. In *Foundations of Modern Auditory Theory.* J. V. Tobias, ed. Academic Press, New York.

SUBJECT INDEX

*Page numbers in italics locate main definition
or principal explanation.*